2016 YEARBOOK

Welcome to the 2016 Airfix Yearbook

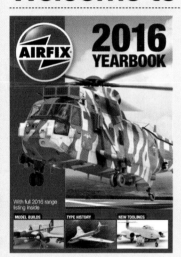

This is our very first edition of the Airfix Yearbook! The best place to find out about the latest products and new releases of 2016. Whether you're just starting out, or an experienced modeller, this publication has everything you need to progress in your Airfix World.

We've had a great 2015 at Airfix, and we're looking forward to continuing and building this excitement and success into 2016. In this Yearbook, you can find handy tips for beginners, as well as builds of our key releases, including the Beaufighter and HMS *Illustrious*. Plus, find out about the Airfix Club and view our gallery for inspiration for your own models, and be amongst the first to see the development images of our star-release, the long-awaited Handley Page Victor. You will also find the list of upcoming products for the 2016 range; however Airfix might have a few surprises up its sleeve…

…The end of 2016 will bring exciting additions to our QUICK BUILD range, the ideal toy for children. There's no paint or glue required as with traditional Airfix kits - you just assemble it like building blocks! Airfix Engineer is another range expanding in late 2016, where you can discover how a variety of engines work by building a working model. Both ranges have proved very popular with the younger generation, and we felt it was important to continue to inspire their creativity. Keep your eyes peeled for the announcement of what these ranges will include!

Stay informed on the latest development updates, release dates and other Airfix information on our social media sites and via Workbench, our fortnightly blog dedicated to giving you the latest news on Airfix releases.

Editor: Chris Clifford
Assistant Editor: Stu Fone
Contributors: Jeremy Brooks, Chris Jones, Ian Hartup, Malcolm V. Lowe, Garry Tobiss, Toni Canfora, Matthew Roberts
Airfix Marketing: Sarah Frame
Art Editor: Tom Bagley
Group Art Editor: Steve Donovan
Production Manager: Janet Watkins

Commercial Director: Ann Saundry
Managing Director: Adrian Cox
Executive Chairman: Richard Cox
Key Publishing Ltd: PO Box 100, Stamford, Lincolnshire, PE9 1XQ, United Kingdom.

Distributed by: Seymour Distribution Ltd, 2 Poultry Avenue, London, EC1A 9PP. Tel: 020 7429 4000. Fax: 020 7429 4001.

Printed by: Warners (Midland) plc, Bourne. Printed in England (ISBN 1910 4154).

Hornby Hobbies Limited:
3rd Floor, The Gateway, Innovation Way, Discovery Park, Sandwich, CT13 9FF, United Kingdom.
www.airfix.com
www.humbrol.com

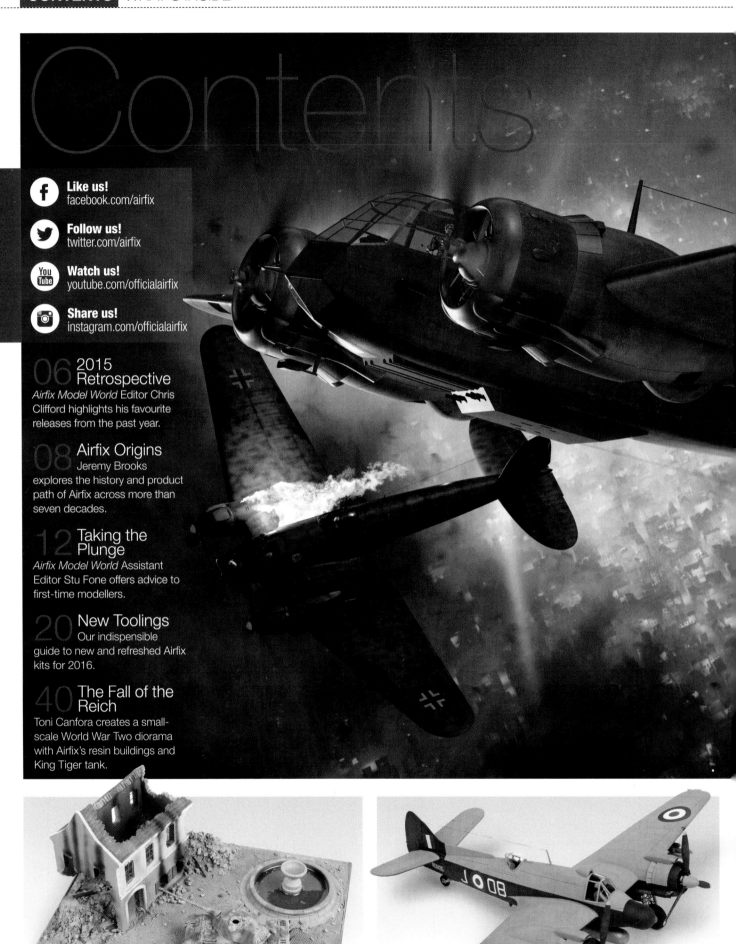

Contents

40

52

20

FULL 2016 RANGE

90

68

Chris Clifford, Editor of *Airfix Model World* magazine, highlights his personal favourites from Airfix's 2015 releases

A Very Good Year

Politicians have been fond of the phrase "You've never had it so good"

But in modelling, we can all recognise the fact that these days this statement actually holds more truth than any election manifesto, in general terms and especially with the wonderful new toolings being released by Airfix.

Arguably, few manufacturers offer such detail and quality for the asking price. And then there are the actual subjects, 2015 being a bumper year. I was delighted with the all-new 1/72 Defiant...a move that pleased many of us who'd soldiered on with limited-run offerings, or the original Airfix product from 1960. It was a great way to bring 2015 in

with a bang, but the good news didn't stop there. With the 75th anniversary of the Battle of Britain on the horizon, Airfix designers knew it was the perfect opportunity to provide the modelling public with fresh 1/48 kits of the legendary Hurricane and Spitfire in Mk.I format. The latter involved a simple re-working of 2014's superb Spitfire

Mk.V tooling, but the Hurricane was completely new and like the Spitfire Mk.V kit, is now widely considered to be the best on the market. Eagle-eyed purchasers of the Hurricane will have noticed spare components in the kit, which signals other releases based on this moulding; one can never have too many Hurricanes!

Terrific twin

Another major and very welcome addition for me has been the early airframe rendition of Bristol's magnificent Beaufighter Mk.X, in 1/72 scale. Many modellers have waited years for a reasonably priced and accurate new tooling of 'The Whispering Death' in this scale, although Airfix's original Beaufighter will have been the focus of countless modelling sessions in the 1960s and beyond. I certainly remember having much fun with it in my childhood.

This new version, though, packs a

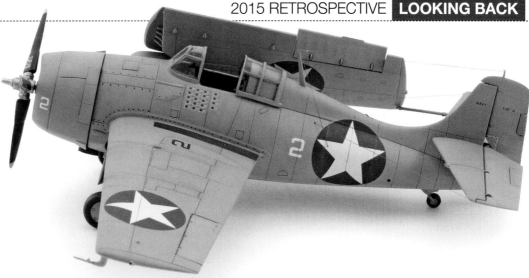

real punch with its accuracy, and all the subtleties of the early Mk.X have been reproduced. And it will have good company soon, in the shape of the 'late' Mk.X and its trademark structural differences, such as the fin fillet and radar-equipped 'thimble' nose. A build of said forthcoming kit features in this very Yearbook.

I feel it's worth noting that Airfix has also catered for more nostalgic tastes with its re-releases of classic kits. It's been wonderful to see the Comet 4C and Boeing 707 mouldings reappear, but anyone who saw Mike Grant's build of the Vickers Vanguard in April 2015's *Airfix Model World*, will appreciate just what a great basis for scratch-building and 'renovation' these kits are, especially with their excellent new decal sheets.

Excitement among Luftwaffe modellers also heightened in 2015 with a newly tooled 1/72 Heinkel He 111P. For this kit, Airfix relied on a new technique in its CAD design process, in the form of Light Radar (LIDAR) scanning; the method is already used widely by film industry special effects wizards, and scanning the real aircraft ensured complete accuracy – something that cannot be said of previous Heinkel He 111s by other manufacturers. Anyone would be hugely impressed with the level of cockpit features in the Heinkel kit and, as with the

previous year's Dornier, Do 17, it offered a world of painting and dry-brushing fun for detail-hounds.

LIDAR scanning has also been employed on Airfix's new 1/72 Commando HC.4 and Sea King HAR.3 kits, so these will set new standards, and the process will also be used on forthcoming items such as the 1/48 Gloster Meteor F.8.

Later in 2015 came a surprising 1/72 addition...Nakajima's B5N2 'Kate' Japanese carrier attack aircraft. This certainly signified an upturn in Airfix's already praiseworthy design work, and copious cockpit detail and beautifully executed wing folds were just two impressive features. But it would not be long before it met its

match in the 1/72 Grumman F4F-4 Wildcat, which displayed equally stunning panel line engraving and detailed wing folds, and an inspired rendition of the type's involved main undercarriage. If pushed, this would get my vote for Airfix kit of the year. Oh, but hang on!...

A long-awaited treat

It is perhaps fitting to close with what is surely Airfix's most important kit in many years...the Avro Shackleton MR.2. Countless modellers may have been tempted to sell their children, pets and other loved ones to secure an all-new Shackleton model.

Thankfully, nothing so drastic is necessary as the company's efforts with this most famous maritime

patrol and sub-hunting specialist are nothing short of stellar. I had the privilege of inspecting the test-shot parts before they were sent to our contributor Jennifer Wright to be built for *Airfix Model World*, and I was dazzled by what I saw. The fuselage packed with busy crew stations, a well-appointed cockpit and bomb bay and super-fine panel lines are just some of the mouthwatering highlights; this is a kit that will undoubtedly become an instant classic.

There's much more to come for 2016 as this Yearbook shows, and I've no doubt that Airfix will continue to push the boundaries and offer superb subjects for us to build and enjoy. Let's all relish the prospect!

Plastic Pioneer

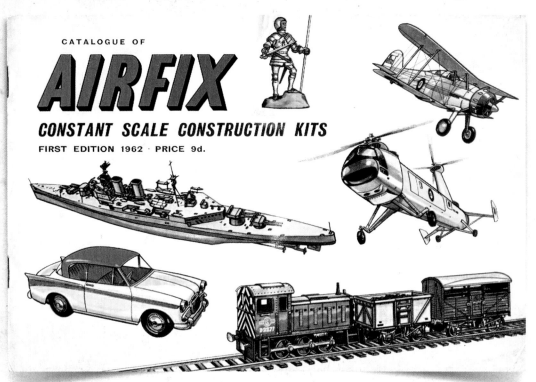

Above: Airfix's first model was of the 408K Ferguson Tractor, produced first for actual Ferguson customers.

Left: Airfix produced its first catalogue of kits in 1962, and a new or updated version has been released every year since.

Jeremy Brooks looks at the history of more than 70 years of Airfix Model kits

Above: The kit that propelled Airfix into dominating the modelling world...the 1/72 Spitfire, BT-K, from 1955.

Right: Airfix introduced 54mm kits of soldiers from 1971 onwards; this Bengal Lancer dates from 1976.

Airfix - Products in Plastic was founded in 1939 and originally made air-filled products (hence the name), toys, lighters and combs for approximately a decade.

After the war, it bought the first plastic injection-moulding machine in Britain and made a series of plastic toys and games, mainly for Woolworth's. In 1949, it was commissioned to make a detailed model, assembled from a kit of parts, of the new TE20 Tractor for Ferguson to give to its customers. Shortly after, Airfix sold the tractor to its existing customers and in 1955 it was sold as a kit. However, this was not the first Airfix kit! In 1952, Woolworth's UK, Airfix's largest customer, asked it to licence-produce a small model of the 'Golden Hind' which was being successfully sold in Woolworth's US stores. After a thorough investigation, Airfix went one better and produced its own moulds. It was sold in a clear plastic bag with a folded instruction sheet and coloured header stapled to it. The first of the famous 'two bob' (10p) kits, it was an instant success and encouraged Airfix to produce more, including a handful of small sailing ships and vintage cars. Eventually more than 1,000 different kits would be moulded during the following six decades.

First 'golden age'

Airfix's big breakthrough came in 1955, when it released a model of the Spitfire. Although it was very inaccurate, with the spurious markings of BT-K, it was enormously popular and showed Airfix that this was where the future lay. Aircraft would eventually fill

more than half the range of kits produced. From 1957, a range of OO/HO railway 'Trackside' kits was introduced, which would prove to be an inexpensive way for railway modellers to add buildings and the like to train sets. The early kits all sold for 2 or 3 shillings (10p or 15p) and could be bought from any branch of Woolworth's, which ensured they soon dominated the British market. A decision to make all kits to a 'constant scale', rather than fit to a box size, made its kits more popular than those of other manufacturers, which often used odd scales.

In 1958, a model of the Lancaster bomber joined the range; this was the first big Airfix kit and it needed larger moulding machines to produce it. A year later, 1/12 scale historical figures and the first 1/600 warships were added to the rapidly growing portfolio, with Airfix producing new kits each month. Distribution was also expanded, to include model shops, newsagents and stores throughout the UK.

The big news for 1960 was the release of the first of many OO/HO armoured fighting vehicles and, to the delight of wargamers, accompanying sets of 48 soldiers, all available very cheaply. Throughout the decade, the range increased and diversified steadily, with modern cars, airliners, large sailing ships, 1/32 soldiers and real space vehicles being produced. The first Airfix kit catalogue was produced in 1962, and a new

Above: Airfix's second large warship, the mighty HMS *Hood*, was introduced in 1960.

Above: Roy Cross' stunning box top for the 1/24 scale Spitfire 'Superkit', released in 1970.

Above: A classic 1960s-style header as designed by Roy Cross, which features the 1968 Ford Model T.

Above: Britain's new 'Bus Stop' airliner, the BAC 1-11, was first moulded by Airfix in 1964.

or updated catalogue has been released every year since. During this period, Airfix employed the artistic talents of Roy Cross and Brian Knight, who would produce some of the most memorable

Above: The Saturn V Rocket was released in 1969, to coincide with the first Moon landings.

artwork to ever grace kit boxes. Even today, those stirring box-top paintings are what older modellers most fondly remember from their early modelling days.

Scaling up

The other parts of Airfix, which produced the motor racing, model railways, Betta Bilda building sets, toys and games, as well as shoes and plastic containers, continued to expand, but to the British public, Airfix was known for one thing only…its construction kits. To the man in the street, any construction kit was an 'Airfix kit'. Even today any article, however large or small, that is made up of assembled parts is usually said to be 'like an Airfix kit'.

The first 25 years is often referred to as the 'Golden Age' of Airfix, and in 1970 it released its first 1/24 scale offering, the Supermarine Spitfire Mk.I…a series that has continued to this day with the release of the

Hawker Typhoon Mk.Ib in 2014. Over the next ten years, more large aircraft kits were released, with ever-increasing detail being added. A survey in the late 1970s suggested that the 1976 1/24 Stuka was the best kit of all time! In 1971, a large 1/12 scale Bentley was added and though it is still available today, no further large car kits were moulded. While aircraft, tanks and ships were still the core of the range,

during the 1970s, dinosaurs, birds, 1/32 tanks and 54mm soldiers also appeared. By the late 1970s, the range had become too large and unwieldy, so Airfix decided to withdraw many kits and reintroduce them on a rotating basis to join a smaller 'core' range. Consequently, while many kits reappear on a regular basis, some, such as those of British garden birds have not been seen since the early 1980s. ➡

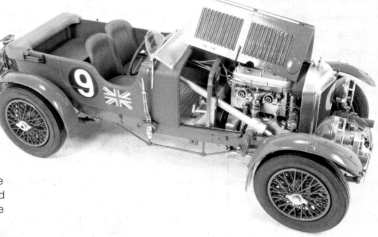

Airfix Timeline

1939 Airfix - Products in Plastic was founded

1949 Ferguson TE20 Tractor commissioned as a kit

1955 Released Spitfire model

1958 First 'big kit' released: 1/72 Lancaster

| 1930 | 1935 | 1940 | 1945 | 1950 | 1955 | 1960 |

Above: The 1960s Hunter kit, upgraded in 1983 by Palitoy, was sold in that company's 'photo' box format.

Below: Airfix's 1977 kit of the Triceratops dinosaur was re-released by Humbrol in 1989.

Above: The veteran 1967 MiG-21 kit was repackaged in the 1990s by Humbrol.

Below: Prior to Airfix moulding its own Sabre in 2010, this Heller kit was re-boxed by Humbrol in 2003.

Fall, rise and fall

Sadly, in 1981, though the kits division was still profitable, Airfix was brought down by a shortage of customers for its various other products and a lengthy dispute at its Meccano subsidiary. Fortunately, the kit side was rescued by General Mills, the American owners of Palitoy, who transferred production to its French factories. For the next five years many US-designed kits, mainly cars, were imported but Airfix did manage to design several new items, most notably the Avro Vulcan in 1983. Then in 1986, General Mills announced it was to pull out of the European toy market and Airfix was sold to

Humbrol, the Hull-based model paint company; it tried to buy Airfix six years before, but was beaten to it by General Mills.

Back in British ownership, modellers had high hopes for new subjects and over the next 20 years, various new kits were moulded in co-operation with

Heller (also owned by Humbrol). Production of existing and new products was undertaken at Heller's Trun factory in France, and many Heller kits were released under the Airfix label and vice versa. A shortage of funding, however, restricted the number of new designs, but Airfix did

mould several new 1/72 and 1/48 aircraft. Later in 1996 and 1997, Airfix released its 1/48 Lightnings and late-mark Spitfires, which were equal in detail to more expensive Japanese designed products, and are still produced today. In 2005 and 2006, models of the controversial TSR.2 and long-serving Nimrod aircraft were announced, along with a Severn Class lifeboat, all to 1/72 scale.

In 2006, the Corgi management team joined Humbrol and brought new ideas and funding...the future looked rosy again. Sadly, the team was not given the chance to implement its ideas, as in mid-2006, the Heller subsidiary, which had been sold but still retained

1960 00/HO scale vehicles and figures range launched

1966 1/600 HMS *Ark Royal* released

1973 1/24 Hurricane joins the 'Super Kit' range

1975 'Best ever' 1/24 Ju 87 Stuka released

1977 Dinosaur range launched

1980 Classic version of 1/72 Lancaster released

1983 1/72 Vulcan released

1986 Airfix sold to Humbrol, collaboration with Heller begins

1960   1965   1970   1975   1980   1985

1/72 FAIREY SWORDFISH Mk.I

Above: Airfix satisfied many modellers' desires with its new-tool 1/72 Fairey Swordfish...

Below: ...and for quarter-scale fans, this wonderful 1/48 Folland Gnat T.1.

1/48 FOLLAND GNAT T.1

all the Airfix moulds, closed. This denied Humbrol's access to these critical components, and forced it into administration. Prospects looked bleak for Airfix, yet once again, a 'white knight' emerged to rescue it, in the shape of Hornby Hobbies, the railway and Scalextric manufacturer.

A new renaissance?
Hornby returned the moulds to the UK and moved all design and development work to its headquarters in Margate, Kent. New moulds were to be made in China and the kits produced in India. At first, several other manufacturers' kits were added to the existing range, known as 'polybagging', while work started in earnest on new-tool projects, and the three previously announced 1/72 kits were completed and released. Hornby had stated its desire to invest more money in the Airfix range and recruited a new design team, which would exploit the latest in computer-aided design processes. Digital artwork was chosen to replace the old 'brush' method of box-top painting and the whole

range was given a fresh, new look.
After 25-year lack of investment, Airfix was back in force! Hornby adopted a policy of gradually replacing older, more popular aircraft kits with new state-of-the-art tools, while adding new subjects to the range. Although several new cars and AFVs have been moulded, the bulk of new releases are aircraft. Kits such as the Shackleton and Whitley have joined the Airfix range for the first time, while others such as the Heinkel He 111 and Lancaster have been replaced by new, exceptionally detailed toolings. Airfix now sometimes employs light-radar (LIDAR) technology to map precisely every subtle shape of the original which, allowing for moulding limitations, results in extremely accurate models. Airfix has returned to designing most of its aircraft

so that several versions can be modelled from a basic tool, and they can be produced in different scales; as an example, it was announced in July 2015 that the new 1/72 Defiant model would be released in 1/48 during 2016.
So we can now look forward to more of the older subjects being replaced, and exciting new kits gracing the shelves, several

of which can be seen in this publication. Airfix has always been famous for producing well-detailed but inexpensive kits... but is now manufacturing items that are considered to be equal to the best in the market, and still at very reasonable prices. Is it any wonder that many modellers are referring to this as a second 'Golden Age'?

1994 Airfix releases first Buccaneer in 1/48

1996 New-tool 1/48 Spitfire F.22/24 released

2006 Hornby acquires Airfix and Humbrol, 1/72 TSR.2 released, 1/72 TSR.2 released

2008 1/72 Nimrod released

2010 1/24 Mosquito FB Mk.VI released

2013 1/24 Typhoon Mk.Ib released

2016 A new Defiant model to be released in 1/48 during 2016

1990 | 1995 | 2000 | 2005 | 2010 | 2015

Taking the Plunge

Airfix Model World magazine's Assistant Editor **Stu Fone** provides a handy guide for starting out in the hobby

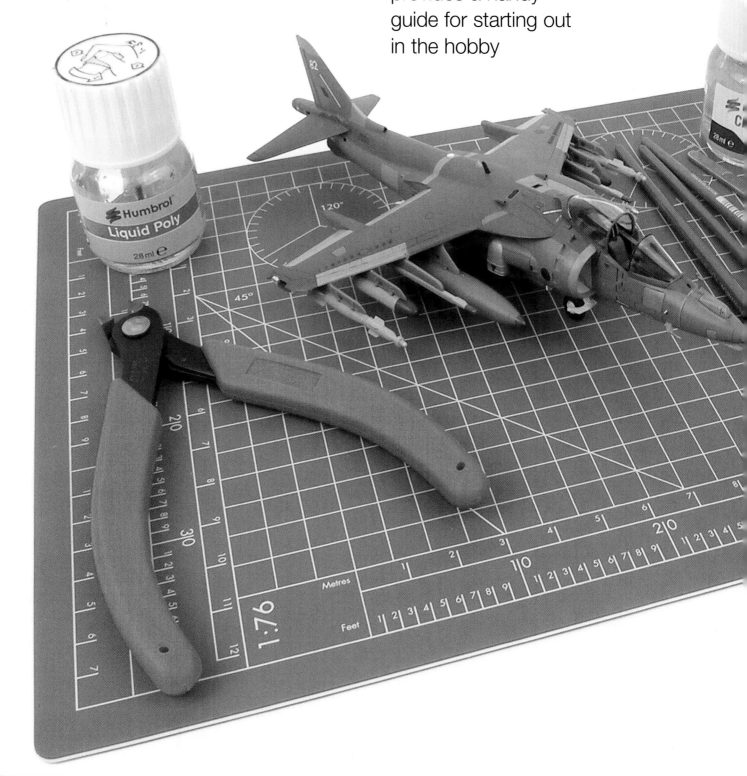

No matter where the inspiration comes from, whether it's a 'make and paint' event, a model show or a friend/relative who already builds models, choosing and building your first kit can be a little daunting.

In this article we cover the basics of kit selection, and the various tools, adhesives, paints and other accessories that will be needed. Hopefully the builds and gallery photographs in this yearbook, or copies of *Airfix Model World*, will provide plenty of inspiration.

Choosing a kit

If you've never built a model before, welcome to the hobby! Modelling is one of the most satisfying, relaxing and ➡

Suggested tools

Beginner
Hobby knife
Tweezers
Cutters
Scissors
Small files
Small flat-bladed screwdriver
Enamel or acrylic paints
Enamel or acrylic thinners
Standard paintbrushes (2, 0, 00)
Cutting mat

Intermediate
Steel rule
Model filler
Wet and Dry paper
Sanding sticks
Pin vice and drills
Masking tape
Decal setting solution
Flat/detail paintbrushes
Gloss/satin/matt varnishes
Weathering washes
Weathering pigments

Advanced
Needle-nosed tweezers
Superglue
Razor saw
Polishing pads/cloths
Scribing tool
Airbrush (and air source)

kits...no matter how colourful they look, and especially if you haven't built a model before. Airfix's extensive range is aimed at various levels of experience and ability (as are those from other manufacturers). These are divided into three main categories: Quick Build (aimed at the really young (see pages 48-49 for details), starter sets and standard kits. The great advantage of the starter sets is they are all-inclusive and provide a kit with the necessary paints, brushes and adhesive. The remainder of the kits are split into series...the higher the series number, the more technical and complex the kit. Beginners should look towards Series 1 and 2 kits, which provide some of the most well-known subjects, such as the Spitfire, Bf 109 and Red Arrows Hawk, then progress to larger kits as you gain more experience and techniques.

Tools

To build any kit a basic selection of tools is essential, but there's no need to buy a mass of new equipment; household items are generally more than adequate to begin with. You'll need a hobby knife for cutting (youngsters should always be supervised by an adult with this) and tweezers for adding small parts. Nail clippers or dedicated cutters are required for removing parts from the runners (sometimes also known as sprues), as are a selection of files for sanding parts and join lines. Fortunately, Humbrol provides a basic tool set as part

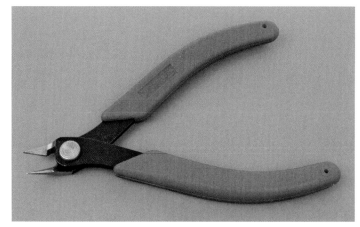

Above: Cutters are an essential part of a modeller's toolbox, and very much simplify the removal of parts from their runners. A basic version is available from Humbrol, although the Xuron cutter shown here has better engineered cutting edges.

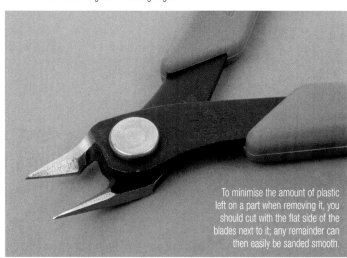

To minimise the amount of plastic left on a part when removing it, you should cut with the flat side of the blades next to it; any remainder can then easily be sanded smooth.

creative pursuits possible, and offers years of enjoyment. As well as exercising your dexterity and teaching the merits of patience, it also gives you a chance to explore the history of the subject.

The first thing is not to be distracted by the larger, complex

of its range, which includes the aforementioned essentials. A small flat-bladed screwdriver is perfect for opening paint tinlets, and can also act as a paint stirrer. Finally, household scissors are ideal for cutting out decals ready for placement on the model.

One investment worth making early on is for a cutting matt, which provides a base for removing parts and placing paints and glues, and more importantly protects the underlying table! Humbrol provides two sizes of cutting mat, with

> "The great advantage of the starter sets is they are all-inclusive"

the smaller A4 version being most suitable for smaller kits and which fits into the Humbrol Workstation, a tray-type item that keeps all of your modelling equipment together.

With most kit parts there will be a small nub of plastic left from cutting the item from the runner. This must be removed before glue is applied, and in most cases a fine file will suffice. To smooth the area further, fine abrasive paper, such as Wet and Dry (it comes in various grades) can be employed. The higher the grade, the finer the paper; for example, 240 is very rough, while 800 or 1,000 are much finer. An alternative is sanding sticks, shaped like large lollypop sticks, but these will conform to curves. Just remember to work through the grades for a finer finish, and add a little water because this helps the abrasive process.

Adhesives

No good kit will go together without glue and the most common type, particularly in Airfix starter sets, is Poly Cement, which comes in a tube and is a general-purpose adhesive. However, it isn't the best for smaller or clear parts as it can be tricky to apply neatly. Thin liquid cement, such as Humbrol's Liquid Poly, will cover most situations but dries quickly, so for larger areas thicker glue is

necessary...such as Humbrol's Precision Poly, which has a fine, needle-like applicator. Liquid Poly bottles have quite large application brushes, so for small parts it's better to apply the glue with a fine paint brush.

Clear kit parts are delicate and prone to marking, so 'kinder'

glues, such as PVA white glue (also known as wood glue), or purpose-made products such as Humbrol's ClearFix, are recommended. Other specialist glues such as cyanoacrylate (Superglue, among other brands) won't be necessary unless metal or resin parts are being added, but

that's most likely to fit into the realm of the more experienced modeller.

Brushes

The right choice of paint brush is vital for good results. Cheap ➡

Left: Decals are generally one of the final stages in a build and most Airfix kits have at least two options, although starter sets usually contain just one. DecalFix is a setting solution which softens the decals and enables them to settle better onto the model's surface.

"Kit decals have made leaps and bounds in terms of quality"

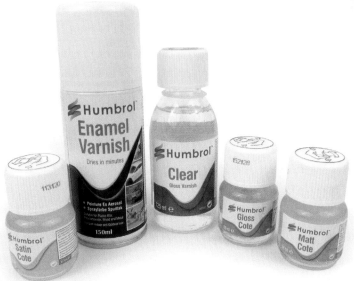

Left: Varnishes are mostly employed to provide a gloss finish prior to the application of decals, and are available as spray cans or bottled products. The latter can either be brushed or airbrushed onto a model. Other sheens enable a final matt or satin finish to be achieved.

paint you will first encounter.

When brush painting, it's better to thin the paint slightly and apply lighter colours first, with two or three thin coats and ample drying time in-between, preferably overnight. This is particularly true for camouflage colours, because if the top coat is applied before the lower has dried, then the two colours will begin to mix as you paint.

There are several brands of varnish available to modellers, and over time, experience will help you to decide which to use, and when. Humbrol's Model Cote solvent-based varnishes, which are available in Matt, Gloss and Satin sheens, are very forgiving and can be applied by brush or airbrush. For those who prefer water-based varnishes, then Humbrol's Clear is ideal. To prevent dust, hairs or

hair brushes shed bristles quickly, so it's better to spend a little more on three or four good sable brushes, rather than six cheap items. Be gentle with your brushes during cleaning and always keep the plastic sleeve over the bristles (if provided) when not in use. Also, it's a good idea to keep a separate bottle of thinner for cleaning brushes used for metallic paints. These generally demand a lot more cleaning as metallic pigment is quite tenacious. Do make sure your brush is spotless after painting, as any traces of the previous colour will ruin your paint finish. As for sizes and shapes, a 2/0 brush is ideal for painting small parts, while a size 2 is good for large areas and general camouflage. Flat brushes are useful for applying varnish as they give better and smoother coverage, but are also excellent

for large areas of colour. In addition to separate items, Humbrol provides the modeller with brushes in packs of four, which include varying sizes and are grouped into differing types (standard, detail, flat and stippling).

Paints and varnishes

Most models demand various shades of paint for their camouflage, and the choice is huge. There are two main types: oil-based enamel, which requires spirit-based thinners for cleaning, and acrylic which can be cleaned (in most cases) with water. Humbrol has a large range of more than 150 shades of enamels, which are more forgiving for brushing, with a slower drying time. Acrylic paint is far easier to clean, but tends to dry much quicker; however, if you are buying a starter set, this is the type of

Left: If anything other than a bare plastic finish is desired, paints are essential. The two main types are oil-based enamels and (generally) water-based acrylics and each has their own type of thinners. To help create demarcations between colours, areas can be masked with either tape or Humbrol Maskol, which is a thick fluid that dries into an elastic covering.

Below: Few proper kits can be assembled without glue, and here are the main types as produced by Humbrol. Poly Cement is available in tube or needle-applicator containers and is a general-purpose adhesive. Liquid Poly is better suited for smaller parts, and ClearFix is ideal for attaching canopies and windows.

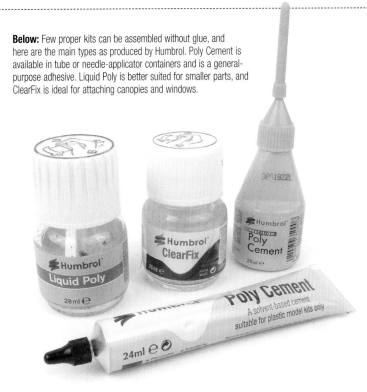

first thing to consider; ideally it should be smooth and glossy to avoid air pockets under the decals. If you've used gloss paint on the model, then varnish may not be necessary but if in doubt, apply a gloss coat before decaling anyway; if the decal is applied to a matt or satin surface, 'silvering' can occur. This is where trapped air betrays itself as a shiny area on the carrier film between the printed portions of the decals. Alternatively, a setting solution, such as Humbrol's DecalFix, can be applied to the surface with a soft paint brush before the decal is positioned; this helps it to soften and 'bed down' onto the model, and conform to raised or engraved detail.

Generally, decals lay individually on the backing, but it's best to cut out and apply just one or two decals at a time to avoid confusion. Use scissors to remove them from the main sheet, and submerge them in a container of lukewarm water until they start to move from the backing. Different

decal brands may require varying release periods, so make sure you read the instructions. Once the decal is ready for application, lift the backing with tweezers, remove the excess water and rest it next to where it should lay on the model. Then gently tease the decal into position with the tweezers or a cocktail stick. If using setting solution, it may need to be applied first and the decal laid over it. The decal will need time to dry and conform to the model, and then it's a matter of patience in applying the remaining decals. If there are many, spread out the process over a few sessions, as if you try to apply too many at one sitting, they can be torn or nudged out of position while handling the model. When all your decals have dried properly, use a damp cloth to wipe away any excess adhesive or water marks. Finally, a top coat of varnish can be applied, which will seal and protect the decals, as well as provide a suitably matt/satin/gloss finish to the colour scheme. ➜

small airborne particles settling on your freshly varnished model while drying, it is advised that you cover it with a plastic container.

Markings

Decals are usually one of the final steps in a build, and will frequently make or break a model's final appearance. The main thing to consider with any decal sheet is thinness; the thinner the decal and carrier film (the backing on which the decals are printed), the more realism will be achieved. Generally, kit decals have made leaps and bounds in terms of quality, but some still possess thick carrier film or may be poorly registered (colours out of alignment). If the latter is the case, it's better to contact the manufacturer for

replacements, or buy new items from after-market companies, rather than endure poor results.

The surface of the model is the

Right: As your skills improve, your toolset will begin to increase in size. Here, more advanced tools are displayed, such as an RB Productions Scribe-R scribing tool mounted in an X-acto handle, and a pin-vice for holding pins or miniature drill bits.

Above: Weathering powders can be added to a model either as a dust with a stiff brush, or mixed with water to create a paste, which can be any consistency, and then brushed or applied with an artist's palette knife depending on the desired effect.

Right: The razor saw is a more advanced tool and is generally used for large-scale cutting or modifications to a kit. They are available in a variety of sizes and can also be used with a mitre-box to create cuts at exactly 45 or 90 degrees to a surface. They are also useful for removing parts from runners when the attachment points are thick.

Above: Pre-mixed washes are a quick and easy method of highlighting engraved panel lines and/or creating streaks on a surface, caused either by the environment (sand and dust), weather (rust) or maintenance (oil streaks).

Moving forward

So far the scope has been kept deliberately simple, but as you get used to building kits and want to try and improve your skills, there are a variety of additional tools and items that can be added to your workbench.

We've already mentioned sanding join lines to make them look smooth, but occasionally this isn't sufficient and a gap or step

"The right choice of paintbrush is vital for good results"

in the seam remains. Filler, such as Humbrol's Model Filler, can then be applied into the gap/step and sanded smooth when dry. For major cutting on a kit, a razor saw (a fine-toothed hand-held saw), is vital. Sizes vary, but the most common are approximately 4 ½-6in (11.5-15cm) in length, with depths of either 1 ¼in (3cm) or ½in (1cm). When it comes to painting, the next step from a brush is the airbrush, which uses a concentrated flow of air to atomise thinned paint and then spray it onto the model. The results are generally much smoother than brush painting, but it takes time to learn how best to thin the paint and use the airbrush without causing the paint to spatter or run. Humbrol's All-purpose Airbrush is perfect for general purpose spraying, with a large-capacity paint jar, but requires additional propellant cans or a compressor for the airflow.

In order to breathe more life and accuracy into your completed model, various weathering techniques can be applied. The simplest is a 'wash', which is basically a mix of heavily thinned paint, and is usually added to highlight engraved panel lines or to portray oil or hydraulic fluid leaks. Similarly, pigments can be applied to simulate dust, dirt or mud, either directly from the container or mixed with water to produce a paste and then added more thickly to the model.

Humbrol's Weathering Powders and Enamel Washes are excellent 'ready-made' solutions, and are available in a number of shades, which can be mixed and applied as required.

So there we have it, a quick introduction to the wonderful world of modelling, which I hope will bring you many hours of entertainment and achievement. Who knows, maybe we'll see some of your models in the Airfix Club or *Airfix Model World* magazines in the future!

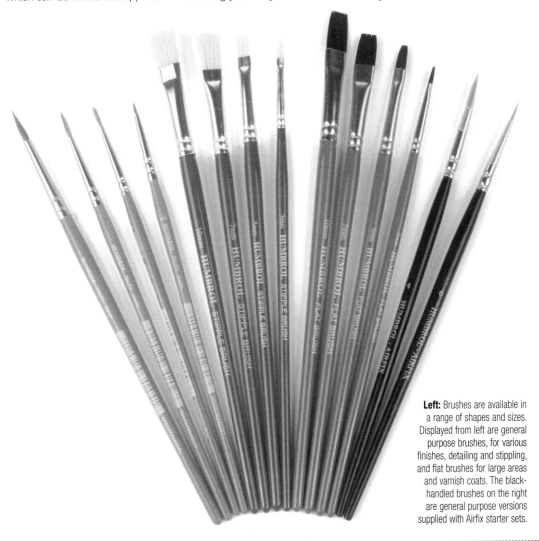

Left: Brushes are available in a range of shapes and sizes. Displayed from left are general purpose brushes, for various finishes, detailing and stippling, and flat brushes for large areas and varnish coats. The black-handled brushes on the right are general purpose versions supplied with Airfix starter sets.

New kits for 2016

V is for Victor

Airfix's flagship
release for 2016 is
the Handley Page
Victor B.2, in 1:72 scale

Colour schemes

- B.2, XL512, 139 Squadron
- B.2, XL189, RAF Wittering

Code: **A12008**

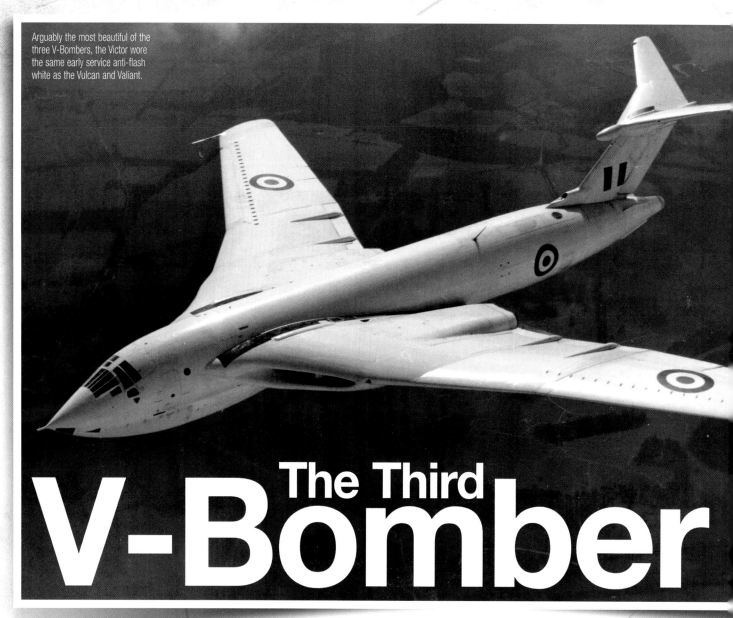

Arguably the most beautiful of the three V-Bombers, the Victor wore the same early service anti-flash white as the Vulcan and Valiant.

The Third V-Bomber

Malcolm V Lowe looks briefly at one of the outstanding post-war jets from Britain's aircraft industry, the Handley Page Victor, particularly in its B.2 nuclear deterrent form

The triumvirate of V-Bombers that defended Britain in the darkest days of the Cold War have rightly gained legendary status in this country's aviation hall of fame. Avro's Vulcan, the Handley Page Victor - and to a lesser extent the Vickers-Armstrongs Valiant - are iconic symbols of Britain's 1950s aircraft industry. All owed their existence to the post-war issue of Specification B.35/46, which envisaged an advanced jet bomber intended to carry conventional or special (atomic/nuclear) weapons, and fly near to the speed of sound at an altitude of approximately 50,000ft (15,240m). In the event, all three manufacturers gained full production contracts for their very different interpretations of the B.35/46 criteria, and Vickers-Armstrongs under the separate Specification B.9/48.

Potent V-Force

Of the three, the Valiant was the most conventional and consequently entered RAF frontline service first, during 1955 with 138 Squadron. It was followed by the delta-wing Avro Vulcan in 1957 (83 Squadron). Handley Page's design was far more complex and innovative, resulting in the type being the last of the three V-Bombers to become operational with the RAF. The most radical feature of its advanced layout was its 'crescent-shaped' swept wing planform, which required much research and the building of a special development aircraft, the HP.88 conversion from a Supermarine prototype, in order to trial this pioneering wing shape. Receiving the company designation HP.80, the new bomber first flew in December 1952, the appropriate name Victor (in keeping with the V-Bomber

theme) being allocated to the new design. The first production version was the Victor B.1, powered by four Armstrong Siddeley Sapphire turbojet engines. In the event this proved to be a fully capable if basic initial production model, and it immediately increased the potency of Britain's nuclear deterrent when the first examples entered service with 10 Squadron of the RAF's Bomber Command at RAF Cottesmore, from April 1958 onwards. These aircraft were intended for high-altitude operations against specific high-value Soviet targets in the event of hostilities between the West and the Soviet Union, a number of nuclear weapons (and conventional bombs) being available for carriage in the large bomb bay that was a distinctive feature of the Victor. Four squadrons eventually flew the type. Several B.1 airframes were upgraded to B.1A standard with

Victor prototype WB775 wore a smart black, red and silver scheme for a time, and it served with Boscombe Down's Aeroplane and Armament Experimental Establishment, and the Royal Aircraft Establishment at Farnborough.

Wittering, formed during February 1962. A second, 100 Squadron, became operational later that year. These were the only two bomber squadrons to be equipped with the B.2, and there were no export customers. The adoption of the Blue Steel nuclear-armed stand-off missile for the B.2 gave the type a very potent long-range strike capability; the aircraft converted to carry this weapon being powered by the RCo.17 Conway 201 and designated B.2R. However, during the Victor's operational life a major change took place regarding the tactics of operating these aircraft. Due to increasingly sophisticated Soviet air defences, a switch was made from high-level to low-level mission profiles for nuclear attack. The Victor B.2 was well equipped with on-board equipment and avionics to allow this, but its airframe was not designed for

sustained low-level operations, and with the increasing deployment of Royal Navy submarine-based Polaris nuclear missiles, the Victor B.2 fleet was depleted until its service exit at the end of 1968.

Total Victor production ran to 86 examples, including two prototype airframes, of which 34 were eventually completed as B.2 bomber sub-types. Nine of the latter were later converted for strategic reconnaissance work, designated Victor SR.2 - sometimes called B.2(SR) or B(SR).2 - to replace similarly tasked Valiants that had been withdrawn due to wing spar fatigue problems. Initial deliveries began during 1965, with the converted aircraft being fitted with various camera combinations and mapping equipment. 'Sniffer' sensors, to detect radiation particles released from nuclear testing, were also

fitted to some aircraft. The operating unit of the SR.2 was 543 Squadron, which finally disbanded at RAF Wyton in May 1974.

A similarly important derivative was the Victor K.2 aerial refuelling tanker, 24 examples eventually being converted by Hawker Siddeley from Victor B.2/B.2R and SR.2 airframes. This proved to be the longest-lived version of the Victor, which served with 55 and 57 Squadrons (and 232 Operational Conversion Unit), and featured a re-designed wing with provision for British-style probe-and-drogue refuelling equipment. The type famously supported Vulcan raids in 1982's Falklands War, and it operated throughout the First Gulf War during 1991, before finally being removed from service in 1993 – making the Victor the last of the three V-Bombers to be retired.

improved defensive electronics, reflecting the need for continuous development in operational capability due to the on-going advances in the Soviet Union's anti-aircraft defences.

Increased power

Although the Victor B.1 was a capable aircraft in its own right, further development led to the more powerful B.2 with a revised wing, among many other changes, to accommodate its very different powerplant of four Rolls-Royce Conway RCo.11 turbofan engines, each of 17,250 lb st (76.8 kN). Typically carrying a crew of four (although this was dependent on mission profile), the Victor B.2 was a big aircraft with a 120ft (36.58m) wing span. The initial example of the Victor B.2 completed its maiden flight on February 20, 1959, and the first unit, 139 Squadron at RAF

It all looks decidedly 'steam-powered' now, but at the time the Victor's busy cockpit was state of the art.

1:72 Bristol Blenheim Mk.If

RE-ISSUE—NEW DECALS

Code: **A04059**

The Type 142 Blenheim was conceived, in part, to satisfy a need for a fast personal transport aircraft for the then *Daily Mail* proprietor, Lord Rothermere. Luckily, Bristol Aeroplane designers were at that time working on just such an aircraft project.

Eventually, approximately 200 Blenheim Mk.I airframes were converted to If format, the main addition being the streamlined ventral gun tray, which held four .303 Browning machine guns. The main role envisaged for the type was that of a long-range day fighter, although ground-attack and bomber escort were other perceived duties. But the appearance of potent German fighters such as the Bf 109, with their greater speed and agility, prompted RAF bosses

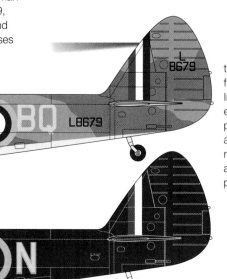

to allocate the If solely to night-fighter missions, where Airborne Interception radar equipment ensured some success. As part of the AI gear, a transmitter aerial was fitted to the nose and receivers were positioned above and below the forward part of the port wing.

Colour schemes

- L8679/BQ-0, 600 (City of London) Squadron, Auxiliary Air Force, RAF Manston, August 1940
- K7159/YX-N, No 54 Operational Training Unit, 1941

1:72 Hawk T.1 Red Arrows 2015

RE-ISSUE—NEW DECALS

(Crown Copyright)

The BAE Systems Hawk is one of the most successful training aircraft of all time, and has been sold to a great many air arms around the globe. One of its most famous exponents is the Royal Air Force Aerobatic Team the Red Arrows, with its nine dazzling red Hawk T.1s. The 'Reds' reached the impressive tally of 50 display seasons in 2014, and wore an appropriate celebratory colour scheme throughout that year. The livery changed yet again for 2015, with a patriotic half Union Jack on the tail, and the white vertical portion leading down into the Reds' trademark white fuselage flash. It was during the winter of 1979-80 that the Red Arrows transitioned from the diminutive Folland Gnat to the Hawk, the former weighing a full-tonne less than its replacement. Since accepting the Hawk at RAF Kemble, the Reds have also been based at Fairford, Scampton and Cranwell.

- Airfix's Starter Gift Set Red Arrows Hawk will also have the same updated 2015 scheme (A55202B)

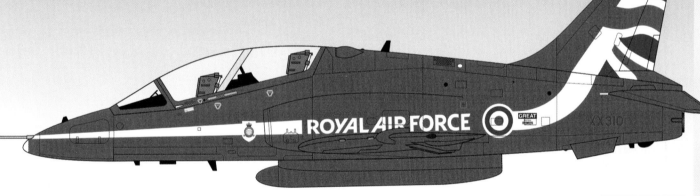

Code: **A02005C**

1:48 Hawker Hurricane Mk.I Tropical

RE-ISSUE–NEW DECALS

While the Hurricane has always stood in the shadow of the legendary Supermarine Spitfire, Hawker's fighter was loved by certain pilots, and it was a very stable gun platform; it could also withstand plenty of punishment. Once the Battle of Britain subsided, the Hurricane was needed beyond Britain's shores to fend off German attacks in the Mediterranean theatre, and it flew missions from Greece, North Africa and Malta.

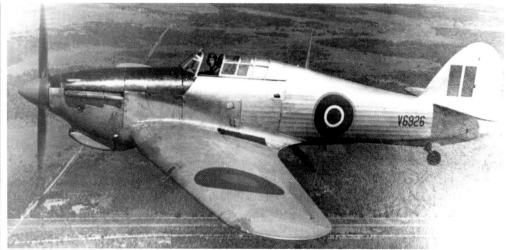

Squadron, led by the famous ace Marmaduke Pattle, supported 80 Squadron at Eleusis in Greece to fend off the German onslaught, but the remnants of both units withdrew to Crete later in the month. They then flew on to Egypt after the battle of Crete in May 1941.

Colour schemes
- V7795, 80 Squadron RAF, Greece, 1941
- T9531, South African Air Force, Rhodesia, 1941

The dusty environment demanded that a special air-cleaning unit be fitted to the front of the aircraft, the Vokes carburettor filter, and this changed the look of the aircraft dramatically...and caused extra drag. The first 'tropicalised' Mk.Is appeared in-theatre after Italy's entry into World War Two, in June 1940. In April 1941, Hurricanes of 33

Code: **A05129**

1:24 Hawker Typhoon Mk.Ib 'Car-Door'

Code: **A19003**

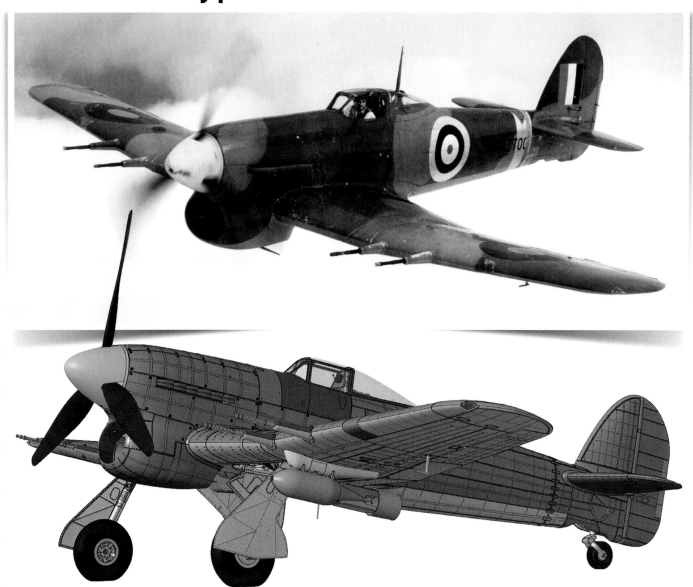

H awker's Typhoon was a mainstay of post-D-Day ground-attack duties with the 2nd Tactical Air Force, and the type soon forged a fearsome reputation with the enemy. Early Mk.Ib aircraft sported the 'car-door' arrangement, whereby the pilot accessed the cockpit via an outwards-opening door on the starboard side of the fuselage, and part of the canopy hinged upwards. This layout hampered pilots' vision, despite a blistered rear-view mirror being added to the top of the canopy, and a clear glazing section replacing the solid aft decking. To remedy the problem, the car door was eventually replaced with a sliding 'bubble' canopy, which afforded a much better view for air-to-air and ground-attack operations. Car-door Typhoons were able to carry 500lb bombs, and targets could include anything from formations of armour to German Navy ships.

Colour schemes
- R7752/PR-G, Roland Beamont, 609 Squadron, Manston, 1943
- RB781/SA-H, 486 Squadron
- EK270/EL-X, 181 Squadron
- JP671/XP-R, 174 Squadron

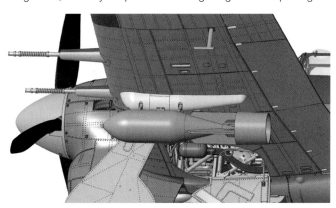

1:48 Gloster Meteor F.8

With its place in history forever marked as the UK's first operational jet fighter, the Meteor became the bedrock of post-war RAF and Auxillary Air Force air defence units. The F.8 variant was arguably the ultimate single-seat example of the type and was recognised chiefly by its restructured tail unit. Australian F.8s went to war in Korea, but the opposing MiG-15 proved a handful for the less nimble Gloster aircraft.

Colour schemes
- WL123, 111 Squadron, RAF North Weald
- WH364, 85 Squadron, 1968

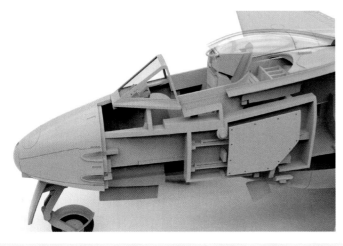

Code: **A09182**

1:72 Code: **A08017**

B-17G Flying Fortress and Bomber Resupply Set

I t was in 1942 that US bombers first joined the Allied air armada against Nazi Germany, but the B-17F that came to the UK in droves was found lacking in forward defensive armament. The remedy was the B-17G, which added a Bendix remote-control turret under the nose; in conjunction with the 'cheek' guns already added to later B-17Fs (carried over to the G-models), this meant that the Flying Fortress could stand up to enemy fighters in a more concentrated fashion. Other improvements included staggered waist guns, to give the gunners more room to operate, and the extended 'Cheyenne' tail turret (named after United Air Lines' modification centre at Cheyenne, Wyoming) with better visibility, sighting and traverse. More than 25 US 8th Air Force Bombardment Groups flew the B-17 from UK air bases, and 8,680 B-17Gs were built in total. But none could operate properly without support from ground equipment, such as the Autocar Tanker, Chevrolet M6 Bomb Truck and Cushman Trike.

Colour schemes:
• B-17G-65-BO, 43-37521 'Skyway Chariot', 351st BS, 100th BG, Thorpe Abbots, March 1945
• B-17G, 43-37993 'Mah Ideel', 401st BS, 91st BG, Bassingbourn

Code: **A06304**

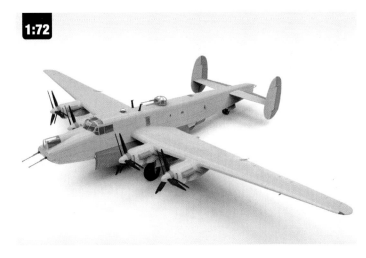

1:72

Avro Shackleton MR.2

Code: A11004

Avro's maritime patrol and sub-hunting aircraft was named in honour of the famous polar explorer Sir Ernest Shackleton, who was a personal friend of the type's designer, Roy Chadwick. The MR.2 variant was a vast improvement over the MR.1, and different features included revised ASV Mk.13 air-to-surface radar (with the fairing moved from the nose to under the rear fuselage), lengthened nose and tail, and twin retractable tailwheels. Its four Rolls-Royce Griffon engines ensured plenty of power and long loiter times, and the MR.2's first user unit was the RAF's 42 Squadron, based at St Eval in Cornwall. Shackletons not only operated from UK bases, but were also in theatre for the Suez Crisis in 1956.

Colour schemes
- WR963/M-B, 224 Squadron, RAF North Front, Gibraltar, September 1957
- WR966/GT/205 'White Knuckle Airlines', 205 Squadron, Tengah Air Base, Singapore, January 1972

de Havilland Mosquito FB.VI

Code: A25001A

A step-change came about with the Mosquito, which was famed for its wooden construction and impressive speed of 362 mph. The FB.VI was developed from the Mk.II fighter prototype, and propelled by Merlin 21, 23 or 25 engines. A load of up to 2,000lb (907kg) could fit into the bomb bay but under-wing rockets also became a part of the arsenal. Aircraft fitted with this weapon formed a major component of RAF Coastal Command anti-shipping operations. One of the most famous actions flown by the FB.VI was the raid on Amiens Prison, but de-armed versions operated by the British Overseas Airways Coroporation flew wartime diplomatic and parts-carrying missions to Sweden's capital, Stockholm.

Colour schemes
- RS625/VV-A
- RS679/UP-A
- RF856/EO-P

RE-ISSUE—NEW DECALS

1:24

1:72

Westland Sea King HC.4

Code: A04056

Famous for its lifesaving role in overall gloss yellow, the Sea King has also been a reliable 'taxi' for the Royal Marines. In the Falklands War of 1982, HC.4s provided sterling service with supply and casualty evacuation flights, and from the Balkans to Iraq, Sierra Leone and Afghanistan, the HC.4 has been a valuable route-to-battle and support asset. It was also on hand to evacuate British civilians and troops from Beirut in 1984. In transportation terms, one 'Junglie' HC.4 could carry a Royal Marines Snowcat tracked vehicle in one go, as an under-slung cargo, and up to 16 troops could be accommodated inside the helicopter. The type has also been fitted with defensive aids and infra-red camera turrets, and other useful features include armoured crew seats, Missile Approach Warners, infra-red jammers and night vision goggle capability.

Colour schemes
- ZF115/R, 848 NAS, Yeovilton 2009.
- ZA314/WT, 848 NAS, Yeovilton 2011

Junkers Ju 87B-1 Stuka

Code: A03087

The term 'Stuka' is derived from the German word for dive-bomber (Sturzkampfflugzeug), and few other wartime monikers instilled such fear in troops and civilians alike. Infamous for its undercarriage-mounted siren, which screamed during dive-bombing attacks to heighten the terror effect. Stukas demanded pilots with nerves of steel due to the steep bombing angle and high-g pullouts. The Ju 87B 'Bertha' was notable for its move to proper wheel spats, and having twice the power of its 'Anton' predecessor. A direct-injection fuel system prevented icing, or engine cut-outs while inverted, while the automatic dive control ensured a pre-set pull-out height, courtesy of a special altimeter.

Colour schemes
- 6G+AT, 9./St.G 51, Norrent-Fontes, France, August 1940
- Kampfgruppe 88, Legion Condor, Spain 1938

1:72

1:72

Fokker E.II

Code: **A01086**

Known collectively across its variants as the 'Fokker Scourge', this company's Eindecker aircraft were Germany's first true fighters and enabled pilots such as Rudolf Berthold and Max Immelmann to become some of the very first aces. The E.II sub-type was a refinement of the previous E.I, and while both had 98 lit main fuel tanks and an oil tank positioned in front of the pilot, the E.II was also fitted with a 22 lit auxiliary fuel tank behind the cockpit. The E.II's nine-cylinder, 100 hp U 1 engine was heavier and larger than the E.I's U 1 powerplant, and the E.II also had a longer fuselage and larger-diameter engine cowling. A maximum speed of 87mph, and single 7.92mm LMG 08/15 machine gun contributed to the E.II's success.

Colour scheme
• 69/15, Kurt von Crailsheim, EFA 53, October 1915

Boulton Paul Defiant Mk.I

Code: **A05128**

1:48

The first production Defiant flew on July 30, 1939 and it fell into the hands of the RAF's 264 Squadron six months later. While it was not the first fighter to be fitted with a gun turret (the Hawker Demon biplane being the first), the concept was refined by the Defiant and its four dorsally positioned .303 machine guns showered enemy aircraft with an unprecedented hail of fire. Despite initial success, the Defiant soon began to fall prey to the Bf 109E, after its pilots ascertained that attacks on the front and belly of the aircraft were safer. This change of fortune for the Defiant prompted RAF top brass to re-role the aircraft to night fighting, with the aid of AI radar equipment, and the decision paid dividends in terms of the UK's nocturnal defences in the winter of 1940-41.

Colour schemes
• L7026/PS-V, 264 Squadron
• L1527/KO-I, II (AC) Squadron

1:72

Westland Sea King HAR.3

Code: **A55307**

The RAF first began to consider operating Sea Kings in the mid-1970s, as a more modern replacement for the Westland Whirlwind HAR.10. While Royal Navy and RAF Sea Kings always had a dedication to Service requirements, around 80 per cent of rescue sorties involved civilian casualties, from capsizing boats to hikers stranded in the mountains. And while the Wessex provided sterling service to the RAF in the search and rescue role, the Sea King offered a massive boost in range and payload. The Golden Yellow HAR.3 (a handful were painted grey for Falklands duty) was developed from the naval HAS.2, minus the anti-submarine equipment, but it still got its power from the same Gnome engines.

Starter Gift Set

Colour scheme
• XZ596, HRH Prince William, RAF Valley, 2011

Royal Aircraft Factory BE.2c

Code: **A02101**

1:72

Approximately 3,500 BE.2s were built and served from 1912 until the end of World War One. The aircraft was designed by the famous Geoffrey de Havilland and ET Busk, and manufactured by the Royal Aircraft Factory, Vickers and Bristol; while its roles included frontline reconnaissance and light bomber, it was also employed in the night fighting arena. Eventually BE2s were flown as a training aircraft after becoming obsolete in actual combat terms. The BE.2 was a stable platform for artillery observation and aerial photography, and could even carry rockets mounted on the wing interplane struts, for attacking Zeppelins. The first pilot to shoot down a German airship over the UK was Captain William Leefe Robinson, who was awarded the Victoria Cross for his efforts.

Colour schemes
• 2693, Leefe Robinson, September 1916
• 8407, RNAS East Fortune, December 1916

1:48 RE-ISSUE–NEW DECALS

EE Canberra B(I).6/B.20

Code: **A10101A**

The Canberra was highly ubiquitous and built in many variants; its lineage is most easily split into 'fighter' and bomber canopy versions. Canberras served worldwide and roles included bomber/interdictor, reconnaissance, electronic warfare and trainer. It set 25 aviation records, and its armament included freefall conventional and nuclear bombs, rocket pods, the AS.30 missile and an underbelly gun pack containing four 20mm cannon.

Colour schemes
- B.(I)6, WT313, 213 Squadron RAF Germany
- B.20, 205, 1(B) OCU, Royal Australian Air Force

Nakajima B5N1 'Kate'

Code: **A04060**

After its initial flight in January 1937, Japan's B5N1 Type 97 first flew combat missions in the Sino-Japanese War, and it proved to be capable at ground-attack. Its limiting factor was inadequate defensive armament, and so it often required a fighter escort when China began to field faster and more potent fighter aircraft of its own. Once the B5N2 took over its role, the B5N1 still proved useful as a training machine, designated B5N1-K. Folding wings allowed more B5N1s to be operated from carriers, and the Hikari 3 engine ensured good reliability.

Colour schemes
- 9-348, 14th Kokutai, 1938-39
- C1-301, 3rd Kokutai, IJN carrier Zuiho

1:72

1:72 RE-ISSUE–NEW DECALS

Supermarine Spitfire Mk.Va

Code: **A02102**

The Spitfire is arguably the most famous fighter of all time, and a great many sub-types were manufactured. Its Mk.V version was the most widely used and most successful, but originally it was purely intended as a stop-gap. An amalgam of the earlier Mk.I/II airframe and the Merlin 45 engine, the Mk.Va was designed to ensure better high-altitude performance in order to combat the Messerschmitt Bf 109F.

Colour schemes
- W3815/D-B, Douglas Bader
- P7666/EB-Z 'Observer Corps', 41 Squadron, Hornchurch, 1941

Bristol Beaufighter Mk.X Late

Code: **A05043**

Known in the Asian theatre as 'Whispering Death', the Beaufighter was one of the best-ever exponents of low-level attack...especially in anti-shipping. The two Hercules engines in the Mk.X generated more than 1,700hp each, to make it one of the fastest ground-attackers, and it equipped RAF Coastal Command squadrons at UK locations such as Dallachy and Banff in Scotland. But World War Two wasn't the only conflict for the type, as it also flew in Operation Firedog...the RAF's response to the Malayan Crisis, in which Communist rebels sought to gain control of Malaya's nine states.

Colour schemes
- Mk.X Late, RD805, 45 Squadron, Negombo, Ceylon, 1948
- TF.X (Torp, Late), RD432/P6-L1, 489 (RNZAF) Squadron, Dallachy, 1945

1:72

1:72

Heinkel He 111H-6

Code: **A07007**

This was Heinkel's most widely used of all the He 111 sub-types. The H-6 could carry two torpedoes, and sported defensive armament of six 7.9mm MG 15 machine guns, and a 20mm cannon. While torpedoes could be wielded, the H-6 was still used for the most part as a bomber, and the debut unit was I./KG 26, which operated in northern Norway, in missions against North Cape convoys, from June 1942.

Colour schemes
- 1H+BP, 6./KG 26, Sicily, early 1941
- W.Nr.7060, 6N+GG, Stab./KG 100, North Africa, spring 1943

1:72

Hunting Percival Jet Provost T.3 `Code: A02103`

The T.3 variant of the Jet Provost was more numerous than any other sub-type of this famous jet trainer. It replaced the propeller-driven Percival Provost as the RAF's first rung of the ladder in terms of jet flying instruction, before the Jet provost T.5/5A became the final version. A more powerful engine (Armstrong Siddeley Viper 102), wingtip fuel tanks and proper ejection seats were trademark features of the T.3, and the type put hundreds of pilots on course to earn their 'wings' via Flying Training Schools.

Colour schemes:
- XM413/24, 2 FTS, RAF Gaydon, 1967
- XM461/11, 1 FTS, RAF Linton-on-Ouse, North Yorkshire, 1984

Grumman Martlet Mk.IV `Code: A02074`

Almost identical to its US-operated F4F-4 Wildcat cousin, apart from a lack of air scoop, a single, wide cowling flap and rounder/narrower-chord cowling, 220 Martlet Mk.IVs were supplied to the Royal Navy via Lend-Lease deliveries. Fleet Air Arm Martlets participated in Operation Ironclad of Madagascar, Operation Torch (the Allied Invasion of North Africa in November 1942), and during 1943 helped to defend the beleaguered island of Malta in the face of heavy Luftwaffe attacks.

Colour schemes:
- FN112/Ø7-D, 888 NAS, FAA, HMS Victorious, November 1942
- FN142/Ø9-P, 893 NAS, FAA, November 1942

1:72

1:48

Junkers Ju 87B-1 Stuka `Code: A07114`

Infamous for its wailing nose-mounted siren, the Stuka was a true menace in the early years of World War Two, but was actually blooded beforehand while flying with Germany's Condor Legion units, on the Fascist side during the Spanish Civil War. The 'B' model was introduced after the 'A' was in production and service for just six months; the former had a more powerful engine (Jumo 211DA), a redesigned fuselage/canopy, enlarged vertical tail and spatted instead of trousered landing gear. Bomb loads of up to 2,205lb (1,000kg) could be carried.

Colour schemes:
- T6+BC, Stab II./StG 2, Bonn-Hangelar, Spring 1940
- Condor Legion, Spain

AW Whitley Mk.VII `Code: A09009`

Production of the Whitley was authorised while the type was still being designed, and it was the most numerous aircraft from Armstrong Whitworth, with 1,814 examples being built. Arguably obsolete by the beginning of World War Two, the type's genesis still progressed and later variants proved to be useful in Coastal Command service; 15 Mk.Vs were also employed by BOAC on supply missions from Gibraltar to the beleaguered island of Malta.

Colour schemes:
- Mk.VII, EB392/YG-R, 502 Squadron RAF Coastal Command, 1942
- Mk.V, G-AGUY, British Overseas Airways Corporation

1:72

1:48

Curtiss P-40B `Code: A05130`

Curtiss' Hawk was the eventual replacement for the US Army Air Corps' P-26 Peashooter monoplane, and the biplanes that came before it. Famed for its earnest defence of Pearl Harbor on December 7, 1941, the P-40B and its derivatives served far and wide, from battling the Japanese with the renowned 'Flying Tigers ' American Volunteer Group in China, to the North African Desert in the hands of RAF and Commonwealth pilots.

Colour schemes:
- P-40B LT George Welch, 47th PS, 15th PG, December 1941 Hawaii
- Hawk 81-A-2, No.47 (P-8127), Robert T Smith, 3rd Squadron (Hell's Angels), American Volunteer Group, Kunming, China, June 1942

1:72 Fokker E.II & BE.2c Dogfight Double BOXED GIFT SET

The Fokker Eindecker and BE.2c both came at a time when airpower had only just been born, and tactics were being learned... but many of the manoeuvres developed by those pioneering flyers are still used by fighter pilots today.

One notable milestone that came with the Fokker involved its armament; until then, machine guns either fired through the propeller (and the blades were fitted with steel wedges to protect them from the bullets), or the gun was mounted over the top wing of a biplane, so it fired over the propeller arc. But an ingenious mechanical method developed in part by the Swiss designer Franz Schneider, and applied in practice by Dutchman Anthony Fokker, synchronised the gun so it would

fire only in between the blades. In mid-1915, the Fokker became a dangerous adversary for the BE.2c and other reconnaissance aircraft, which were poorly armed, and so these were eventually employed in the training role. A famous pilot associated with the Fokker was Oswald Boelcke, who flew all of the E-Series Fokker Eindeckers and scored his third victory in an E.II.

Code: A50177

BOXED GIFT SET

1:72 Ju 87 Stuka & Gloster Gladiator Dogfight Double

I f two aircraft epitomised the early stages of World War Two, it would be the Stuka and Gladiator...but for different reasons. While the former exemplified Germany's 'Blitzkreig' warfare, via its destructive and terrifying dive-bombing raids, the Gladiator was in the twilight of its career. The type was the last of the RAF's biplane fighters, but it was outclassed and suffered greatly during the German advance through France and into Norway. Yet it could still mount a dogged defence when in the right hands, and this was demonstrated ably by Sea Gladiator pilots, who helped to protect the beleaguered island of Malta during German and Italian air attacks in 1940.

Code: **A50179**

1:72 Battle of the Somme Centenary

Fokker E.II, Royal Aircraft Factory BE.2c (with stand), British and French soldiers, diorama base

BOXED GIFT SET

The order for thousands of British troops to advance across an 18 mile wide stretch of frontline trenches into No Man's Land (and into a storm of bullets and shellfire) on the first day of the Battle of the Somme is now notorious.

Heavy German artillery bombardment produced many casualties even before the whistles blew, and the British battle plans faltered further due to the intense enemy fire experienced during the advance. The Somme was one of the most heavily defended German-held areas along the Western front, and much preparation beforehand had been done to make life difficult for the 'Tommies'. Well-positioned German machine guns ravaged British troops, and this first day of the battle, July 1, 1916, changed the way the British Army fought future actions. Aerial reconnaissance played its part in the battle though, through aircraft such as the BE.2c, but it was a hazardous undertaking with German Eindeckers - the famous 'Fokker Scourge' - on patrol.

Code: A50178

1:72 Pearl Harbor

BOXED GIFT SET

Mitsubishi A6M2 Zero, Nakajima B5N2 'Kate', Curtiss P-40B

Japan's actions in the Sino-Japanese War were costly, and so it sought to secure raw materials from outside its islands and expand its influence across Asia; the nation also signed the Tripartite Pact to join the Axis powers, which immediately put it at odds with the USA and Great Britain. Its surprise attack on the US Navy base at Pearl Harbor, Hawaii, was a bid to destroy the US Pacific Fleet in one go and the act was branded "the Day of Infamy" by US President Franklin D. Roosevelt. Japanese aircraft from the carriers *Akagi, Kaga, Soryu, Hiryu, Shokaku*

and *Zuikaku* wrought havoc at Pearl Harbor, with bomb and torpedo attacks, and Zero fighters flew escort to protect against US fighters.

The US response was brave in the face of such weighty opposition, as P-40Bs, P-36s and anti-aircraft gunners shot down more than 15 Japanese aircraft. It was in vain, though, as the Imperial Japanese Navy dealt a crippling blow to the Pacific Fleet...but the attack did bring the USA into World War Two, to fight alongside British and Commonwealth forces.

Code: A50180

The Fall of the Reich

Award-winning modeller **Toni Canfora** uses Airfix buildings and a King Tiger tank to create this convincing World War Two scene

Stock codes: **A75016/A75018/A03310**

1: Airfix's ruined restaurant and city fountain came in cream-coloured resin. The casting was excellent and both items needed just a very minor clean-up before painting could commence.

2: After a wash in soapy water, and a rinse, the building and fountain received a coat of grey surface primer. This was necessary to help the paints adhere.

3: It was decided that the house should be painted in two different colours for the first and second floor. The lower section was painted first in a sand colour, with a wide, flat brush.

4: Next, a bright yellow accent was chosen for the second floor. This created a clear, but not too dramatic contrast. Yellow has a low opacity, so several layers had to be applied.

5: With the walls painted it was time to tackle the tiled roof. A suitable colour was mixed and again applied with a brush to avoid over-painting the already finished areas. For greater variety, several brighter and darker nuances can be used.

6: Bright blue doors and window shutters brought further life to the building. Again, very careful painting with a fine brush was necessary.

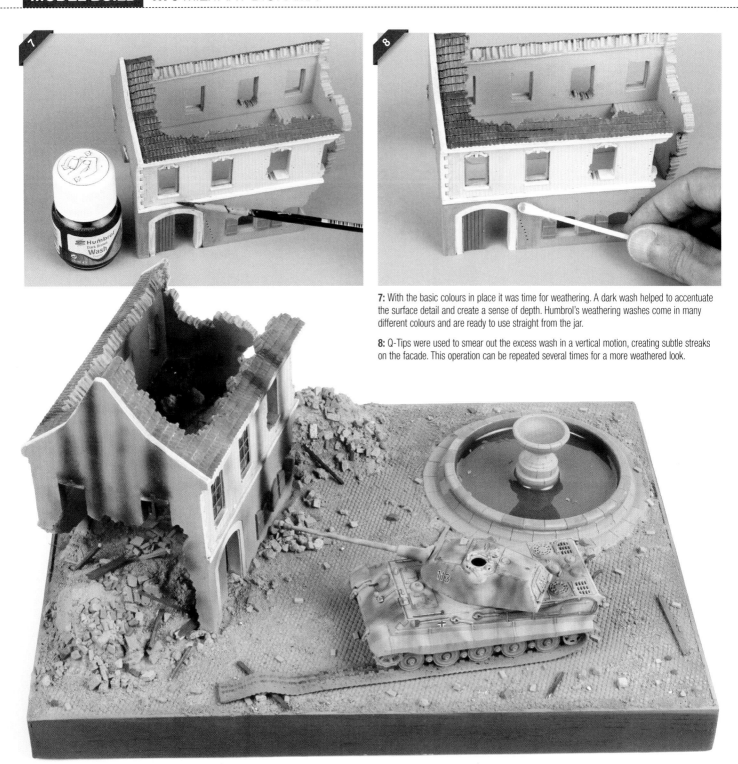

7: With the basic colours in place it was time for weathering. A dark wash helped to accentuate the surface detail and create a sense of depth. Humbrol's weathering washes come in many different colours and are ready to use straight from the jar.

8: Q-Tips were used to smear out the excess wash in a vertical motion, creating subtle streaks on the facade. This operation can be repeated several times for a more weathered look.

9: The interior faces were also painted in separate colours, although little of them would be seen on the finished model. Here, a green coat has been applied to the walls on the second floor, and light grey on the first. Washes have also been brushed onto the roof.

10: Falling debris from a collapsing house would create a great amount of dust in various colours. Weathering powders were ideal to simulate this, particularly in a small scale. They were applied with a brush in a stippling motion.

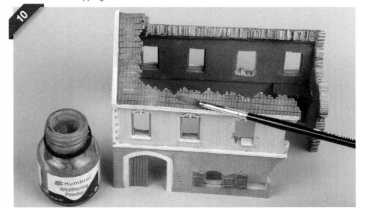

11: Weathering powders were also used for the smoke trails from the window openings, and they were brushed vertically in several layers. Care should be taken though, as the powders are difficult to remove should the modeller change his or her mind.

12: The beautifully cast fountain was painted in a variety of grey nuances for a more interesting look. This was followed by careful dry-brushing to make the surface appear somewhat weather beaten. The centre piece was painted in a more beige tone to create variety.

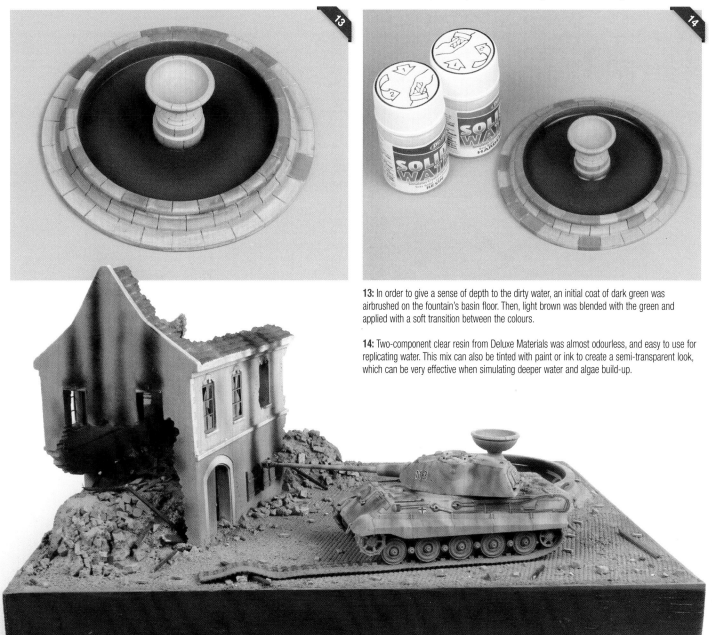

13: In order to give a sense of depth to the dirty water, an initial coat of dark green was airbrushed on the fountain's basin floor. Then, light brown was blended with the green and applied with a soft transition between the colours.

14: Two-component clear resin from Deluxe Materials was almost odourless, and easy to use for replicating water. This mix can also be tinted with paint or ink to create a semi-transparent look, which can be very effective when simulating deeper water and algae build-up.

15: The PE window frames just required a little sanding and they were ready for paint. For the burnt windows on the house, the frames were painted black, while the clear acetate windows were cut with scissors to simulate broken glass.

16: Windows were installed without any difficulties since the fit was perfect. An immediate effect on the house was evident, as the glazing created a more detailed overall appearance; the operation was repeated on the rear of the house.

17: The base for the diorama was cut from foam insulation board, which is available in various thicknesses. A pre-stamped cobblestone sheet was found in a railway modelling shop and proved to be very suitable for this little scene.

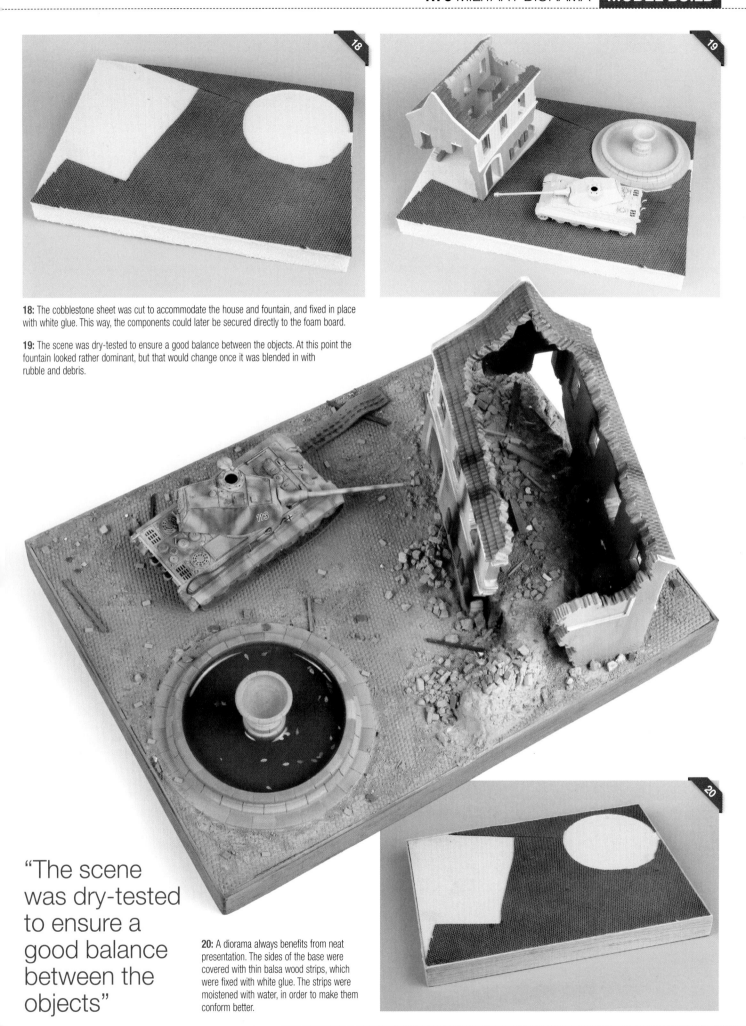

18: The cobblestone sheet was cut to accommodate the house and fountain, and fixed in place with white glue. This way, the components could later be secured directly to the foam board.

19: The scene was dry-tested to ensure a good balance between the objects. At this point the fountain looked rather dominant, but that would change once it was blended in with rubble and debris.

"The scene was dry-tested to ensure a good balance between the objects"

20: A diorama always benefits from neat presentation. The sides of the base were covered with thin balsa wood strips, which were fixed with white glue. The strips were moistened with water, in order to make them conform better.

21: The interior of the house would be filled with lots of rubble. In order to create volume quickly, two pieces of foam board were glued in place to form a base.

22: Several nuances of brown and beige served as a base for the colour of the debris. They were applied in subsequently lighter tones to create depth. The rest of the base also received a thin mist coat at this stage.

23: The house was then fixed to the base. Sand and rubble helped to blend the house into the environment and diluted white glue was once again used to set it on the base.

24: The fountain had been left off the base during the work with the house and rubble, in order to protect the fragile resin surface.

25: More debris and loose tiles, bricks and rubble were placed over the surface to tie everything together. It was vital to make this a random pattern, or it would look too staged and unnatural.

26: Several thin coats were misted onto the base to simulate a generally dusty environment, although it muted the detail slightly.

27: To reinvigorate the surface, a fine brush was used to pick out smaller details among the debris. Bricks, stones and other pieces of rubble were painted various shades of red-brown, sand, beige, grey and white.

28: The final acts on the fountain were to add a touch of green to simulate the remains of water on the centre piece, as well as adding paper leaves on the water's surface.

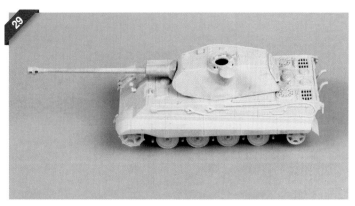

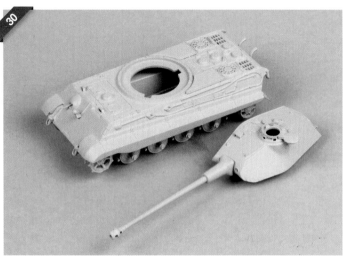

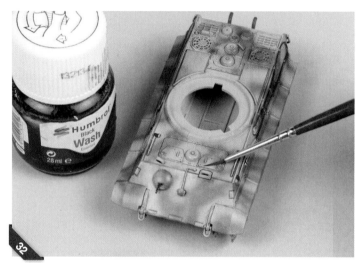

29: Airfix's 1:76 King Tiger is an impressively moulded subject, displaying very fine surface detail. Apart from a rather complex running gear and chassis, it was a quick and straightforward build over the course of two evenings. The gun was posed at a low elevation to further the air of crew abandonment.

30: The model received a coat of grey primer before painting commenced. Primers don't just help the paint to adhere...they also reveal surface flaws that can be treated.

31: A first coat of yellow was followed by green and brown camouflage. In this scale it's important to keep the colours light, and to apply the camouflage in very thin layers or the model can easily look like a die-cast model.

32: Humbrol's enamel washes once again came to good use when accentuating the surface detail. The entire model was first given a thin coat of clear varnish, to help the wash flow better and to protect the surface.

33: Smaller details such as the tools were picked out with acrylics and a fine brush. Very subtle chipping was added with a sponge, and streaks were applied with artist's oils.

34: The tracks were painted with black primer, followed by dark brown, and finally weathering powder. They were slightly tricky to position, but once they were fixed with cyanoacrylate glue, all was well.

35: The Airfix King Tiger tank was very light, and in order to make it sit tightly to the cobblestone paving it was fixed with a screw, into a drilled hole in the base plate.

> "Smaller details such as the tools were picked out with acrylics and a fine brush"

36: One of the tracks was left in a position to simulate a breakdown, as often seen in real combat photos. Rubble was placed underneath the track, which was then secured with cyanoacrylate glue to force it into the bent position. It was then blended in with weathering powder.

KitStarter

The Airfix
KitStarter concept
allows vintage
tooling to be
reintroduced on a
limited basis

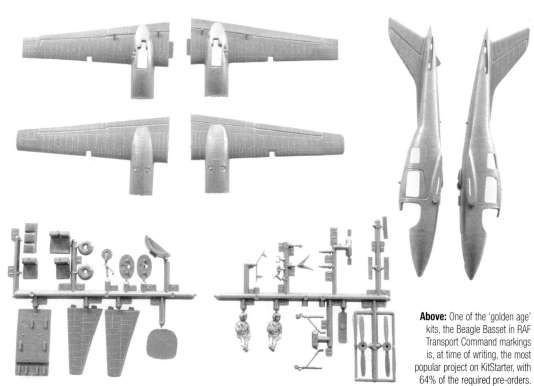

Do many of you cast a nostalgic look back and remember the Airfix kits you built all those years ago...those that are no longer in production and increasingly hard to find?

There is a chance to get them again, albeit on a limited-run basis (and only if the moulds are in a useable condition). This is the rationale behind the KitStarter programme. Modellers nominate a kit on the Airfix forum, and if enough interest is shown, it will be

Above: One of the 'golden age' kits, the Beagle Basset in RAF Transport Command markings is, at time of writing, the most popular project on KitStarter, with 64% of the required pre-orders.

selected as a 'project'...the moulds will be checked and repaired, and if all goes well then pre-orders can be placed. When a certain level of backing is reached, the kit will go into limited production. Note that it will just be available to those who have placed one or more pre-order 'bids' – it won't be offered for general release.

What will you receive if your suggestion and bids are successful? You will be supplied with the kit in a plain box, plus the original-style instruction leaflet... and a trip down memory lane when you build it!

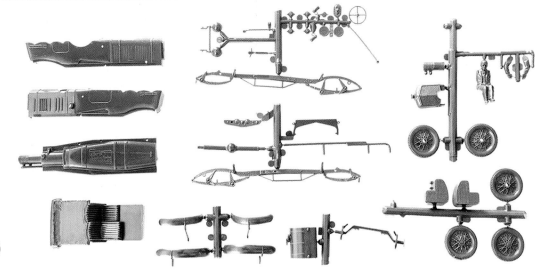

Above: Perhaps the biggest element of the nostalgia will be getting your hands on the original parts...these for the 4.5 Litre 1930 Bentley (originally released in 1956) do show how far the hobby has come in the past six decades.

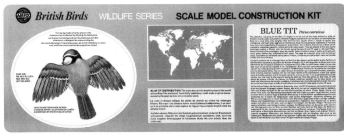

Above: Should any of the British Birds kits be re-released on a limited basis thanks to KitStarter, they will include the original colour data panel, complete with painting guide.

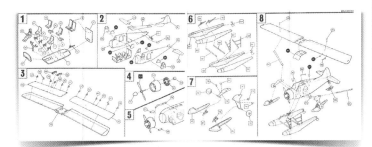

Above: For those of you more familiar with the current crop of Airfix instruction leaflets, with individual stages, the older-style sheets may come as something of a surprise!

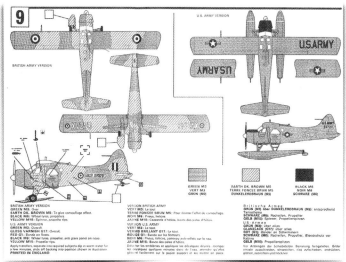

Above: All of the kits will be issued with prints of their original instruction leaflets, and they will be manufactured in the UK to ensure a short lead time.

For many modellers, it will be a chance to once again enjoy vintage classics such as the 1:72 DHC Beaver.

Firedog Rocketeer

Chris Jones builds Airfix's forthcoming 'late' version of the Beaufighter Mk.X

1 and 2: Despite the new content, the internal parts remain unchanged so work began by assembling the cockpit and wing spars. All internal areas were airbrushed with multiple thin coats of Humbrol 78 Matt Cockpit Green. The use of cellulose thinner helped to speed drying time, but as with any airbrushing, the use of a respirator mask is advisable to avoid inhaling noxious fumes.

Stock code: A05043

A irfix's new Bristol Beaufighter TF.X (Late) combines the contents of 2015's 'early' release, with all the parts needed to represent the later version of the TF.X on a brand new runner. The new elements include a thimble nose, dorsal fin fillet, propeller spinners, Mk. VI Rocket Projectile rigs, 200 gal fuel tank and an F.46 strike camera fairing, which sits behind the cockpit on the fuselage spine. This particular airframe wears the smart two-tone ground-attack colours of the RAF's post-war deployment on 'Operation Firedog', during the Malayan Emergency.

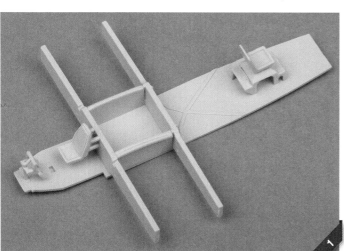

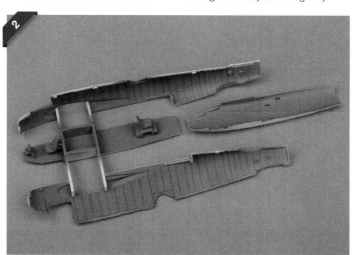

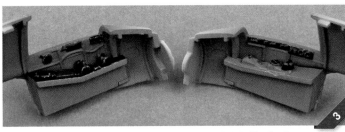

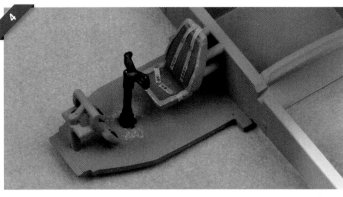

3: After painting the relevant side consoles in Matt Black, Humbrol 27 Matt Sea Grey was used to dry-brush the raised detail, before chipping was added with the aid of a silver pencil.

4: Seatbelts were added with small strips of craft/hobby masking tape. After painting the harnesses, a 2B pencil was used to draw on detail.

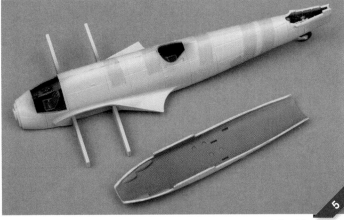

5: The fit of the main fuselage halves was noteworthy. After adding the cockpit floor/wing spar assembly, the underside fuselage insert was attached. It was important to remove paint from the mating surfaces to ensure the glue had sufficient surface area to bond together.

6: As the assembly of the main airframe components came together, some of the new (and most distinctive) elements present for the TF.X (late) version came into play; the thimble nose and dorsal fin fillet.

7: After sanding the seams on the wings and fuselage, the entire airframe was brought together, with just minimal filler being required in a small number of places. The overall fit was very good indeed.

8: The engines were attached separately, before adding the cowl parts around them. After ensuring the underside cowl join touched, the slight gaps between the other cowl parts were covered fully by the scoops and exhaust fairings. The cowl ring ensured neat alignment. ➡

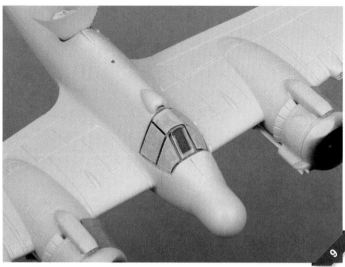

9: For awkward curved areas of canopy framing such as on the windscreen, a helpful approach was to use extremely thin strips of craft/hobby masking tape, which were then carefully filled in by Humbrol Maskol.

10: With all masking complete, it was possible to start the painting process.

11: Humbrol 33 Matt Black was airbrushed over the entire airframe, before a thin mottle of 27 Matt Sea Grey was sprayed on top.

12: Matt Black was then mixed 34 Matt White and mottled over the airframe to provide extra emphasis to the fading.

"Humbrol 165 Medium Sea Grey was applied in multiple thin layers over the black"

13: Thin strips of craft/hobby tape were used to provide a sharp demarcation between the black and grey areas of the airframe. A cocktail stick was used to burnish the tape in all areas, to prevent paint 'bleeding' under the edges.

14: With the time-consuming task of masking the outline completed, the remaining areas were carefully filled in with more tape.

15: Humbrol 165 Medium Sea Grey was applied in multiple thin layers over the black, before a thin mix of the same paint and white was mottled on top to represent fading and provide visual interest. Although it's better to spray dark colours over lighter shades, it was easier to mask over the black in this instance.

16: Production decals weren't available at the time of building, so Freightdog Models kindly stepped in with its excellent 'Brits Abroad Pt.II' sheet (FSD72004S). These were applied after the model was sprayed with acrylic gloss varnish, which helped to prevent the decals from 'silvering'...a frustrating phenomenon that occurs when tiny air bubbles get trapped between the decal and matt/rough paint underneath. ➡

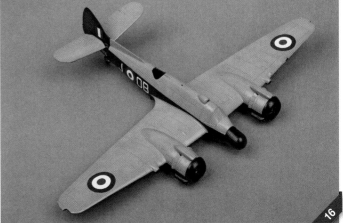

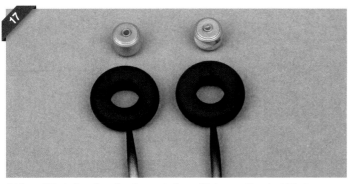

17: To avoid the tedium of masking, it was actually possible to assemble and paint the tyres separately from the rims, which saved time and effort. The tolerance was tight but with gentle pressure, a perfect snap-fit was achieved.

18: The white codes were eye-catching on the black underside. At this stage, as much final assembly took place as possible before the decals were sealed with more gloss varnish.

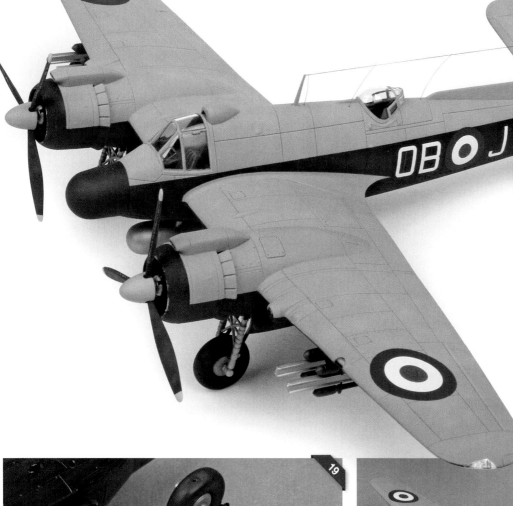

19: Assembling the undercarriage took time and care, but with sufficient planning and test-fitting a decent result was achieved. It was found that adding the wheels to their legs without glue, and before any other assembly took place, was more advisable than adding the wheels once the entire strut framework had been built, to avoid breakages. Liquid cement (applied with a tiny brush to the axles) was suitable for fixing the wheels in place once the legs were set and the weighted flat spots were aligned.

20: With the decals on and sealed, the gorgeous post-war bomber scheme really came to life!

"With the decals on and sealed, the gorgeous post-war bomber scheme really came to life!"

21: The Mk. VI Rocket Projectile rigs were one of the key new additions in this kit. It was vital to drill out the relevant locating holes earlier in the build to ensure final assembly was as easy as possible.

22: Multiple thin coats of matt varnish were applied to mute the final finish. The fading on the grey areas showed through in a subtle manner, but in this instance the fading on the black was 'lost in translation' somewhat. However, with the benefit of spare time, careful post-shading can be used to add or enhance these kinds of effects...even when a build is effectively finished.

23: A pin-vice and drill bit made miniscule holes, before each end of a piece of E-Z Line fine black elastic thread was dipped in Superglue accelerant and attached to tiny drops of Superglue on the aerial mast and tail. Smoke-coloured invisible mending thread was then used to add the whip aerial and other wires.

24: A silver pencil was used to add chipping to the propeller blades and cowl rings. Although a .303 Browning was provided in the kit, it wasn't utilised during final assembly. These were removed from Operation Firedog Beaufighters after a navigator managed to put holes in his own aircraft's tail!

Post-War ■
Freighter

Garry Tobiss completes
Airfix's Dakota Mk.IV in the
smart livery of Dan Air

DAN – AIR SERVICES LTD

Stock code: **A08015**

1: The Douglas Dakota Mk. IV (A08015) is a new-tool kit and an extension of the previously released C-47 from 2014. It comprises five runners in grey-blue styrene, one clear parts frame, a decal sheet plus instructions. As this is a recent tooling, the detail is of high quality.

2: The interior for the cabin was for the military C-47 version; post-war civilian Dakotas were a mix of ex-forces C-47s and stock DC-3s, and so their interiors would vary. But little of this detail would be visible after the build so it was not an issue.

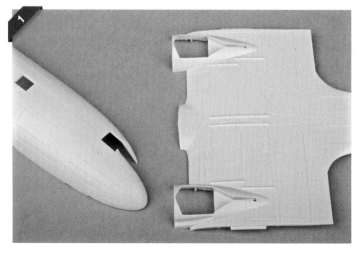

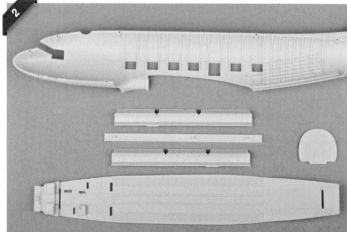

Kit Colour Schemes

- Dan Air Services Ltd
- Dakota G-ACGB BOAC 1943

Above: Two civilian markings options are offered, one being a colourful Dan Air Services aircraft, G-AMSU, based at Blackbushe Airport, Hampshire, England, in 1955. The second is a camouflaged wartime machine, G-AGKN, operated by the British Overseas Airways Corporation, in 1942. ➜

"As this is a recent tooling, the detail is of high quality"

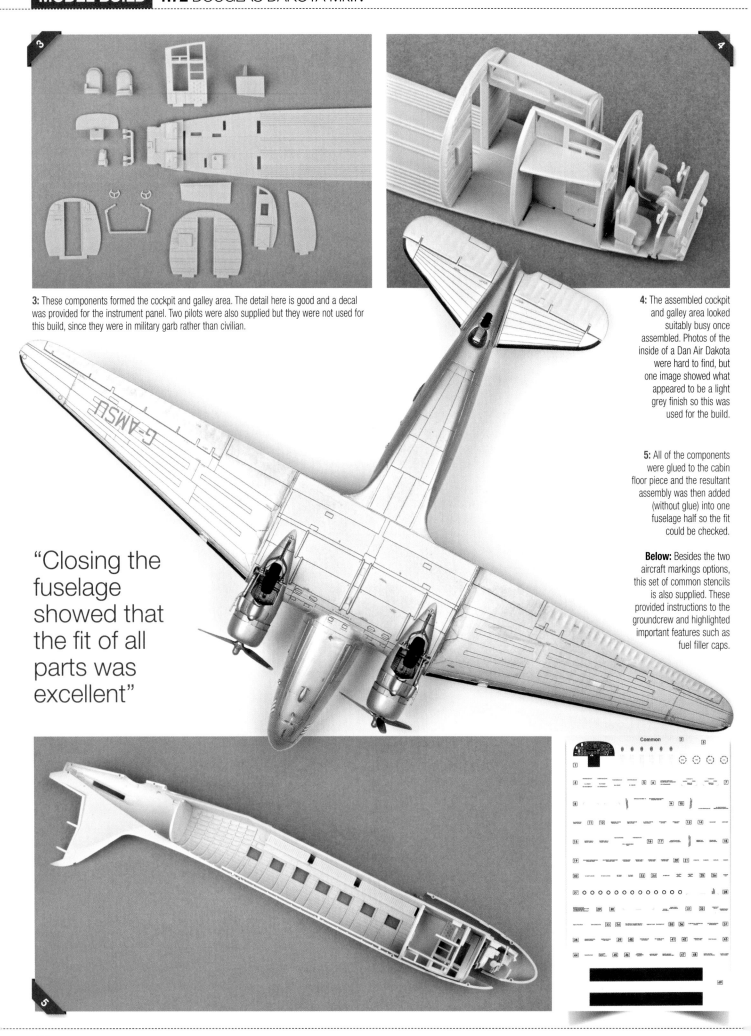

3: These components formed the cockpit and galley area. The detail here is good and a decal was provided for the instrument panel. Two pilots were also supplied but they were not used for this build, since they were in military garb rather than civilian.

4: The assembled cockpit and galley area looked suitably busy once assembled. Photos of the inside of a Dan Air Dakota were hard to find, but one image showed what appeared to be a light grey finish so this was used for the build.

5: All of the components were glued to the cabin floor piece and the resultant assembly was then added (without glue) into one fuselage half so the fit could be checked.

Below: Besides the two aircraft markings options, this set of common stencils is also supplied. These provided instructions to the groundcrew and highlighted important features such as fuel filler caps.

"Closing the fuselage showed that the fit of all parts was excellent"

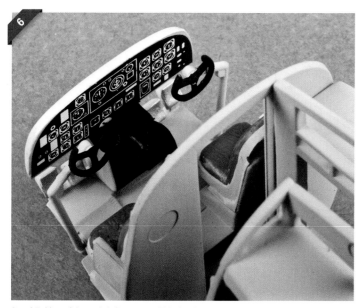

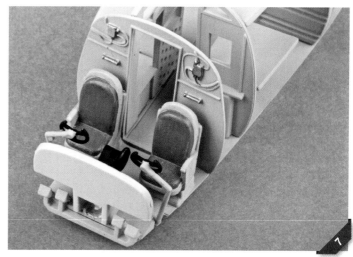

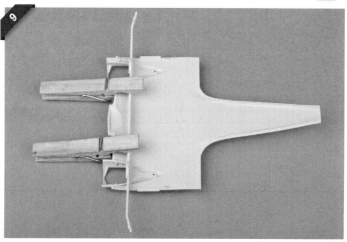

6 and 7: Most of the cockpit features would be hard to see once the fuselage was glued together, but it was still fun to bring the area to life with various colours. These were all best guesses, but guided by references from later Dan Air airliners.

8: A large wing spar was supplied together with the lower central wing section. Each end of the spar also had an integrally moulded landing light. Very minor adjustments to the spar were required to make sure the upper and lower wings joined correctly.

9: The spar was glued to the lower wing and pegs were used to ensure the parts were completely in contact. This was important, because the spar was designed to ensure the wings would set at the correct angle.

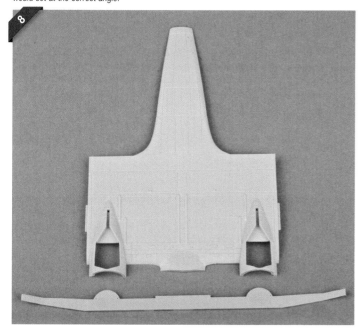

10: Closing the fuselage showed that the fit of all parts was excellent, and everything was held together with masking tape until set. The lower wing was then added but not glued at this stage, to ensure alignment with the fuselage sides was correct. ➡

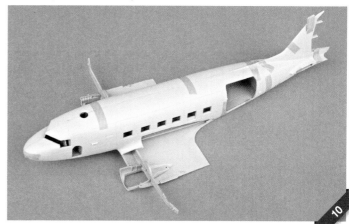

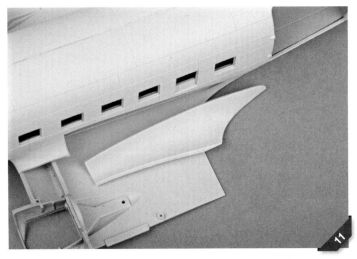

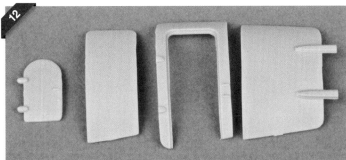

11: A fairing on the top of each wing root was provided to create the curved trademark profile. A small amount of filler was eventually required to deal with tiny gaps between the upper wing and fuselage.

12: Passenger and cargo doors were depicted faithfully. These could be posed open or closed and were left until after the clear pieces had been added, just in case the latter ended up in the fuselage; bigger holes meant they would be easier to retrieve!

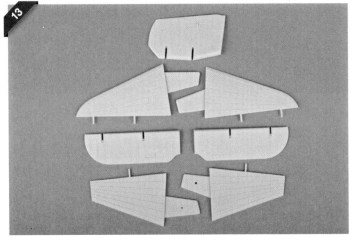

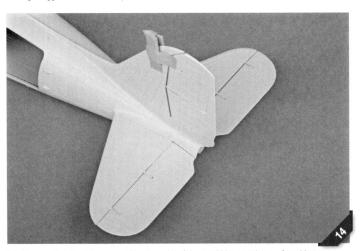

13: These components are for the rudder and stabilisers. The latter locked together when fitted through the fuselage, although tape was still needed to keep them in the correct position until the glue had set.

14: The completed tailplane assembly; control surfaces could be posed as preferred but were kept neutral for this build. Note the wood and tape cover on the vertical stabiliser, fashioned to protect the delicate aerial during construction.

15: Five parts made up the wings, and the central lower section (shown in previous photos) meant there were no join seams to deal with along the under-fuselage centre. Plenty of fine panel line engraving adorned the wing surfaces.

16: These were the main components for the two Pratt & Whitney R-1830-S1C3G Twin Wasp 14-cylinder radial engines. The driveshaft design meant the propellers could be added after painting was completed…very useful.

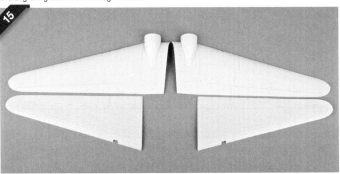

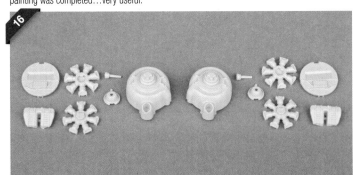

"A two-piece cowling was provided for each engine"

17: A two-piece cowling was provided for each engine. The interior of each received grey primer, followed by Humbrol 56 Gun Metal. All Humbrol paints used in the build were acrylic – excellent for beginners because the brushes can be cleaned with water.

18: Each fuel tank was added into the wheel well behind the engine. The instructions suggested Humbrol 154 Signal Yellow for these, which was very bright, and so everything was weathered with a dark wash – this also highlighted all the moulded detail.

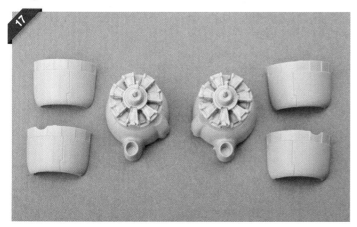

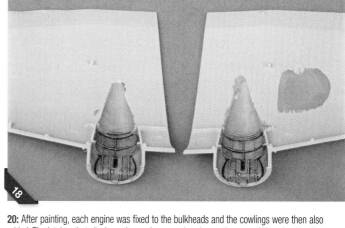

19: The engines were highly visible on the finished model, so each was painted with Humbrol 56 Gun Metal, followed by a grimy oil wash to accentuate the moulded features. Humbrol 11 Silver highlights were then added.

20: After painting, each engine was fixed to the bulkheads and the cowlings were then also added. The intakes that sit above the engines are also shown; these would be glued in place once the engines were attached to each wing.

G-AMSU

Built originally as a C-47B and with the military serial 44-77216, G-AMSU was acquired from Meredith Air Transport by Dan Air in May 1953.
It was repainted around 1960, with a solid cheatline, and eventually the aircraft was withdrawn from service in March 1968 and dismantled for spares in 1970. This image captures G-AMSU possibly in 1965. *(Tom Singfield Collection)*

21: A selection of the clear parts provided in the kit. These were all dipped in Humbrol Clear and then left to dry overnight. This protected the parts from scratches and also gave them extra shine. The fuselage windows were designed to be added from the outside.

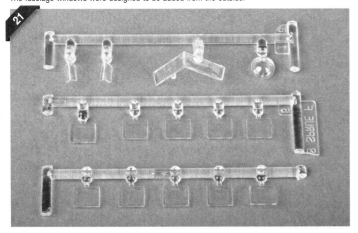

Below: These were the main paints used for the build, but grey primer was applied first to check for imperfections as natural metal finishes are very unforgiving. Polished Aluminium Metalcote was added next, while the model sat in a large open-topped cardboard box and the spraying was done outside while wearing a respirator.

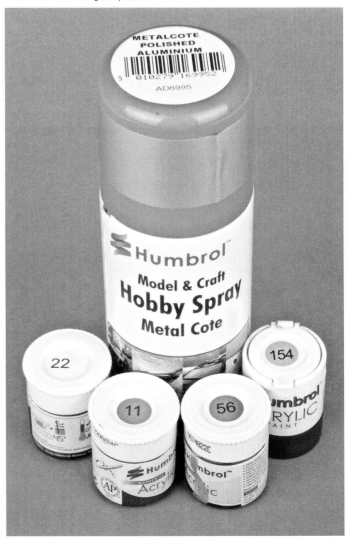

22: The main paintwork was applied via Humbrol spray can and an airbrush, so all clear parts were masked. A commercially available masking set and liquid mask were used, which saved a great deal of time and effort. Only very tiny amounts of filler were necessary on the wing root seams, which were sanded gently with fine abrasive paper.

23: After leaving the paint to cure for 48 hours, the model was masked and Humbrol 22 White added via airbrush, with the paint applied in several thin coats. A layer of Humbrol Clear was then hand-brushed to provide a smooth finish – particularly for the white areas. This coat was then sanded gently in preparation for the decals.

24: All the decals went on easily with the aid of softening solution, but there were many stencils for an aircraft of this scale so patience was required. Another coat of Clear sealed the decals, while the anti-glare black paint on the nose was hand-brushed, because the shape of the area was defined by the edges of the decals.

25: The undercarriage was well detailed and each main tyre was moulded to simulate the effect of weight. Note also the small amount of exhaust staining plus the effects of a dark wash to highlight panel line detail. This was deliberately understated – if an airliner looks too worn then passengers won't want to fly in it!

"Each main tyre was moulded to simulate the effect of weight"

Club Class!

Join the Airfix Club from just £15 per year to access exclusive news and views from Airfix plus a whole host of member benefits

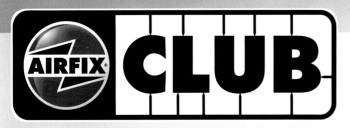

10% DISCOUNT on Airfix brand products*

NEW JUNIOR SECTION

including lots of fun activities, competitions and facts!

Your Membership Includes...

- 10% discount* at Airfix.com for the duration of your membership
- Club welcome pack with membership card and Airfix Flying Hours passport, on all postal membership
- Entry to the Airfix Flying Hours scheme – collect tokens from Airfix kits to exchange for FREE models
- Access to exclusive Airfix Club kits – only available to Club members
- £20 voucher** to spend on exclusive Airfix Club kits
- 3 Club magazines and one winter edition
- Competitions including chances to win entry to events and brilliant prizes
- Discounted entry to various UK attractions
- Junior section with competitions and news

*discount applies to full price items
**cannot be used in conjunction with any other offer

£20 VOUCHER
to spend on club exclusive models – online and over the phone**

For more information please call our dedicated club helpline **01843 233512** or e-mail us at **newclubs@hornby.com**

Lusty at Large

Stu Fone tackles Airfix's imposing 1:350 HMS *Illustrious*...one of the biggest kits in the range

Stock code: **A14201** Gift Set: **A50059**

HMS *Illustrious*, affectionately known as 'Lusty' to her crew, was the second of the Invincible-class through-deck cruisers and the fifth ship in the Royal Navy to bear the name.

Completed too late to participate in the Falklands War, she subsequently served in the Middle East, Balkans, Levant and West Africa, with a mixed rotary and fixed-wing air component of up to 22 aircraft, before it was converted into a helicopter carrier. In 2014, at the ripe old age of 32 (at that time the oldest ship in the fleet), *Illustrious* was decommissioned,

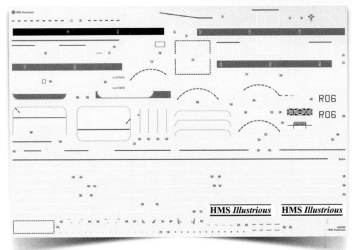

The decal sheet provided full deck stencilling and markings for the aircraft and helicopters. All of the decals were slightly thick, but this prevented 'bleed through' of underlying colours. Applications of Humbrol DecalFix solution during decaling ensured that the process was simple, and that the markings conformed to any raised features.

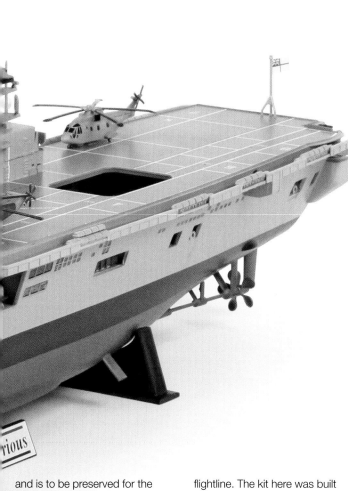

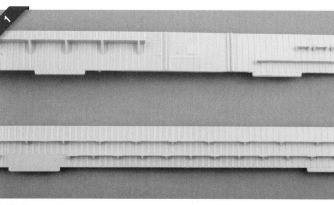

1: The first area to be worked on was the hangar, and the walls featured plenty of detail with moulded balconies, ladders, piping and equipment boxes. It also meant the choice of raised or lowered lifts had to be made early on, and the latter was chosen for interest and to display the fine interior.

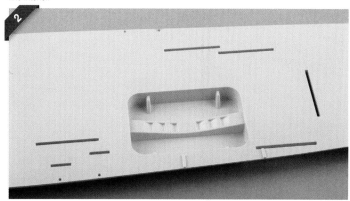

2: Airfix's attention to detail extended all the way to the hangar floor, with recesses for the lift raising/lowering arms, which closely resembled those spaces on the ship.

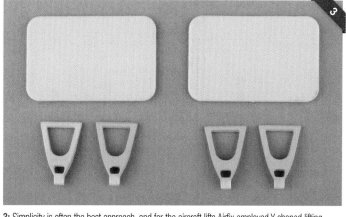

3: Simplicity is often the best approach, and for the aircraft lifts Airfix employed Y-shaped lifting arms as on the real vessel. Coupled with the notches in the deck floor, these would enable the lifts to be positioned at three different heights...separate panels were provided for fully raised platforms.

and is to be preserved for the nation as a museum at an as-yet unknown location.

Airfix's 1/350 HMS *Illustrious* was released in 2010, and packs an amazing amount of detail into the box. In addition to a composite air wing of Sea Kings, Merlins, Sea Harriers and Harrier GR.9s, deck-handling tractors and a crane are included to enliven the flightline. The kit here was built out-of-the-box and portrayed 'Lusty' in 2009, although the Sea Harriers were not used as this type was retired from service in 2006. While the occasional element was challenging, overall this was an enjoyable build and provided plenty of opportunities to try new techniques. ➜

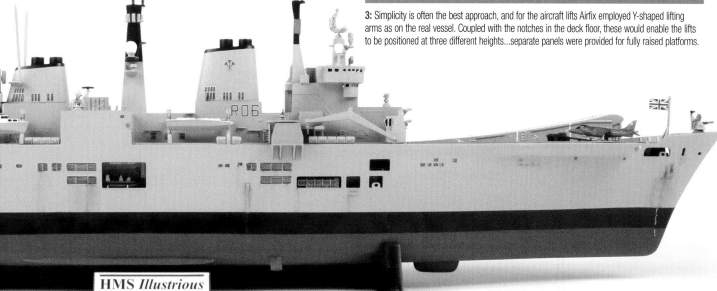

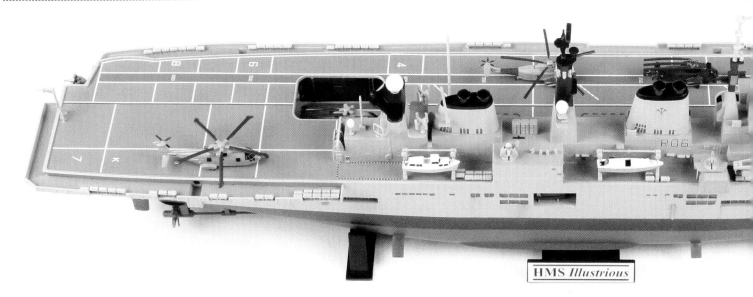

HMS *Illustrious*

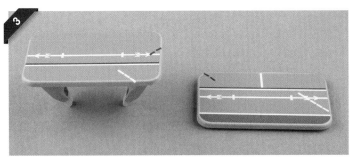

3: The lifts were painted Humbrol 64 Matt Light Grey and the raising/lowering arms in 130 Satin White. Once dry, the lifts received Humbrol Enamel Gloss Varnish Spray, and decals were applied an hour later; despite the matt carrier film, a pre-coating of the surface with DecalFix ensured a smooth finish and the absence of silvering.

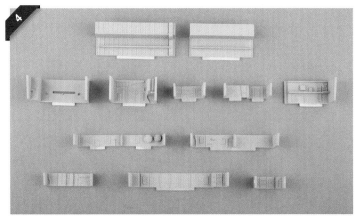

4: While the lift assemblies were drying, attention turned to the hangar walls and the various hull bays. All featured excellent detail, with watertight doors, heating ducts, piping and cable/hose reel units.

5: After a base-coat of 127 Satin US Ghost Grey, the heating ducts were painted with 27003 Polished Steel, which was buffed to a shine once it had cured. A mixture of 33 Matt Black and 98 Matt Chocolate was then thinned heavily and employed as a wash, to highlight detail and accentuate any shadows.

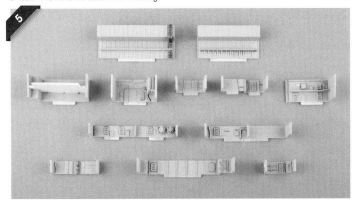

6: Reference images indicated that the hangar walls adjacent to the lifts were painted black, and this was replicated with Matt Black ahead of the raised detail being dry-brushed lightly with white. The deck was airbrushed with 64 Matt Light Grey, before the sides and completed forward lift were added, with the Y-shaped arms on the latter fitting neatly into the notches.

7: Here the parts for the hull bays on one side of the ship have been prepared for painting. A deck-mounted crane was provided for the smaller rigid-hull inflatable boat (RHIB), while the larger craft had a bigger roof-mounted assembly. The gate-like components are boarding ladders, with two mounted on each side of the ship.

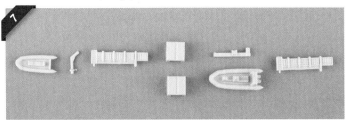

8: Each bay was built separately, with smaller parts added before the roof was attached and the components clamped to ensure a strong join. The small RHIB received a base coat of 127 Satin US Ghost Grey, with the inflatable sections then painted black and 27 Matt Sea Grey, in accordance with reference photographs.

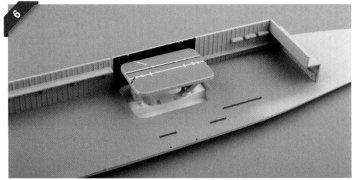

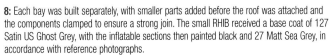

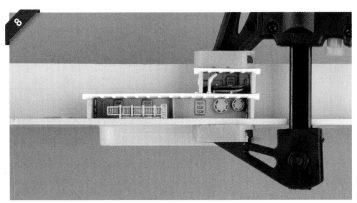

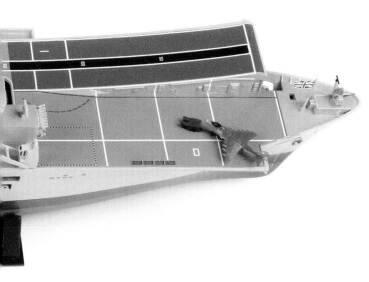

11: For a kit as large as this, great care must be taken when mating the hull halves, as these long sections can be prone to warping. To ensure a good fit and strong join, the underside was added at the same time, and was secured with masking tape before clamps were employed to ensure the sides fitted correctly.

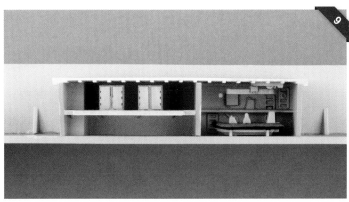

9: The large RHIB was been painted in the same manner as its smaller version, and the roof-mounted crane received a layer of 127 Satin US Ghost Grey, before detail features were picked out with a black/brown wash.

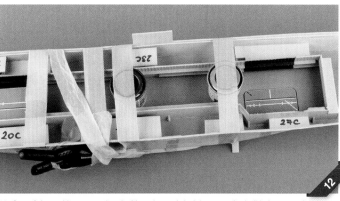

12: One of the problems associated with an internal deck between the hull halves was that it could be pushed upwards while the sides were assembled/held. It was found that tins of enamel paint, placed on the hangar floor and braced with masking tape, were the perfect counter to this, and provided sufficient downward pressure to keep the deck in place. ➜

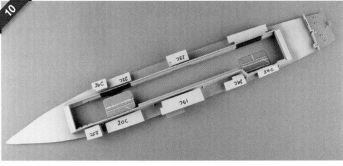

10: Part numbers were written on the hull bay roof sections before they were removed from the runner and airbrushed, which prevented confusion when the bays were assembled. The area at the stern was painted with 64 Matt Light Grey at the same time as the hangar floor, with raised features being picked out with 127 Satin US Ghost Grey.

"The deck was airbrushed with two coats of Humbrol 64 Light Grey"

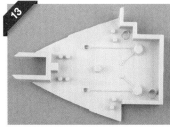

13: The anchor deck was reproduced faithfully, with raised-relief anchor chains and bollards, and the support structure for the upper deck Goalkeeper close-in weapons system. Several mould release marks needed to be sanded smooth before this item could be painted.

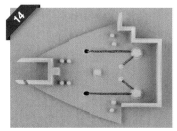

14: This area was painted in the same manner as the hangar and hull bays, with horizontal surfaces in 64 Matt Light Grey; raised features and vertical surfaces were then coated with 127 Satin US Ghost Grey. The anchor chain was picked out with 27003 Polished Steel, and buffed to a shine.

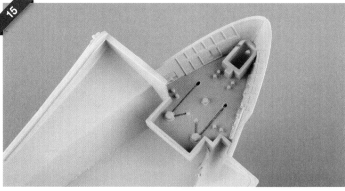

15: Once the hull had dried overnight and the clamps and masking tape had been removed, the anchor deck was dropped into place and secured with Liquid Poly. Care was taken to ensure the rear bulkhead aligned correctly with the flight deck overhang.

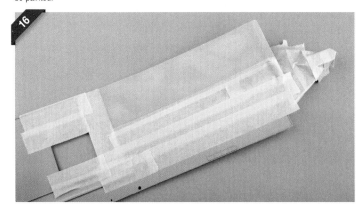

16: Effort then turned to the flight deck and superstructures. The deck was airbrushed with two coats of 64 Light Grey, and then the ski-jump section was masked and sprayed in 27 Matt Sea Grey. The deck was left for two days to cure properly, before it was married to the hull and secured with Humbrol Liquid Poly.

17: The lower hull was primed with 64 Light Grey to check for any blemishes, and these were filled with Humbrol Model Filler and sanded smooth. Prior to airbrushing the main 127 Satin US Ghost Grey hull colour, the entire flight deck and all of the hull bays were masked. Foam packing, cut to size and pushed into the openings, was particularly useful for the latter areas.

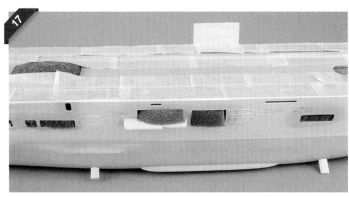

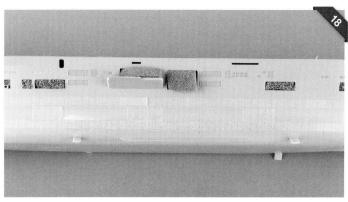

18: 'Lusty' had a distinctive thick black 'boot line' along the hull. Thin masking tape was positioned on the lower/upper hull join and lengths of tape added above it to ensure the upper tape was parallel, before the boot line was airbrushed black. The gap was estimated from the waterline markings (decals 17 and 29).

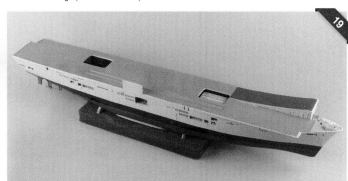

19: The bottom of the boot line acted as a guide to masking the lower hull, which was airbrushed with several coats of 70 Matt Brick Red. To seal the paint and prepare for the decals, the entire hull was coated with Enamel Gloss Varnish Spray. This was excellent, as it dried quickly and provided a hardy, glossy surface.

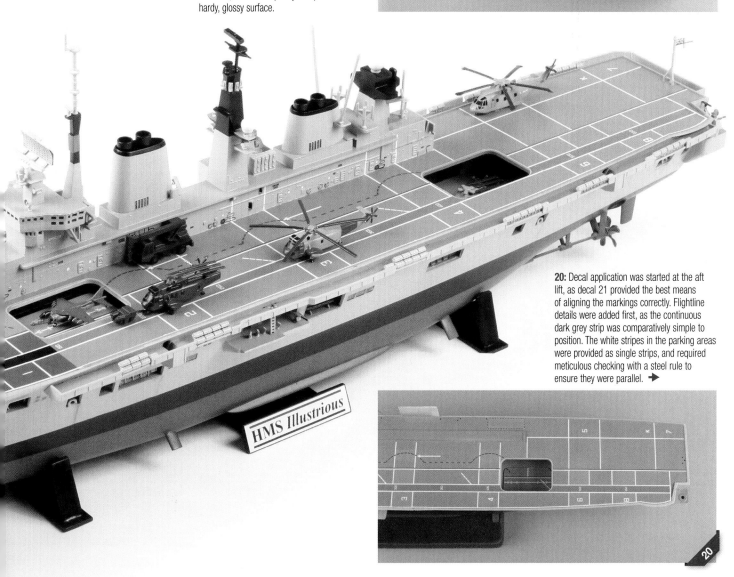

20: Decal application was started at the aft lift, as decal 21 provided the best means of aligning the markings correctly. Flightline details were added first, as the continuous dark grey strip was comparatively simple to position. The white stripes in the parking areas were provided as single strips, and required meticulous checking with a steel rule to ensure they were parallel. ➜

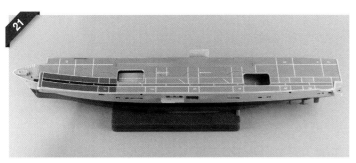

21: After two mammoth decal sessions, the deck and hull was completed. Judicious application of DecalFix ensured that, despite the large areas of clear carrier film between several of the deck lines, there was no silvering and the markings had a 'painted-on' look. The foam mat was positioned under the hull throughout to protect the fragile stabilising fins.

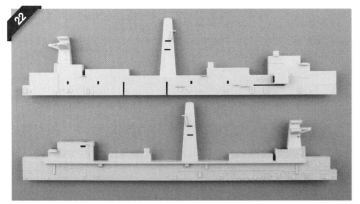

22: *Illustrious*' superstructure was provided as longitudinally split halves, which meant extra care was taken during assembly. However, this enabled Airfix to include a surprising amount of detail on the sides, all of which would benefit from careful painting and application of washes.

"The superstructure received a light coat of Enamel Satin Varnish Spray before the main detail painting commenced"

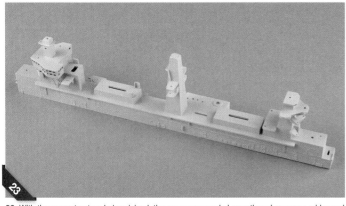

23: With the superstructure halves joined, the seam was sanded smooth and any gaps addressed with Humbrol Model Filler. The interior of the bridge sections were painted black and then assembled, before the entire structure was first sprayed with 127 Satin US Ghost Grey. When dry, horizontal surfaces were painted 64 Light Grey.

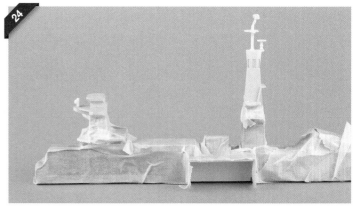

24: A characteristic of modern warships is that the highest areas, particularly the masts, are painted black. To replicate this, the majority of the superstructure was masked and the uncovered areas airbrushed. Note the eight antenna fairings on the main mast were not added until after this area had been sprayed, as they are a similar colour to the hull.

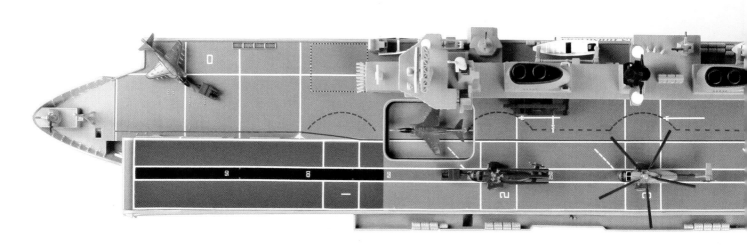

HMS *Illustrious*

25: After the masking had been removed, smaller items, which included various communications and navigation radar antennas, were added. Any areas of overspray or where black had seeped under the masking tape were neatened at this time.

26: The superstructure received a light coat of Enamel Satin Varnish Spray before the main detail painting commenced. Spare white decals from the deck markings were used for the stripes, while the rest of the fire hoses, fuel lines, light housings and door surrounds were hand-painted with various Humbrol shades, based on reference photographs.

27: In a deviation from the instructions, the funnels were assembled, complete with exhaust stacks, and then airbrushed 127 Satin US Ghost Grey, before the upper sections were masked and sprayed black. The intake grilles were treated with a black/brown wash, followed by Humbrol Dark Grey Wash in the corners, which provided tonal variation.

28: Similarly, the deck-edge walkways were treated as sub-assemblies, and received the same colour scheme as the superstructure. To create contrast on the life-raft containers, the recesses were given a pin-wash of dark grey, before the raised rings were dry-brushed with a mix of 127 Satin US Ghost Grey and white. ➡

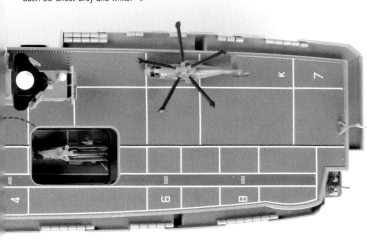

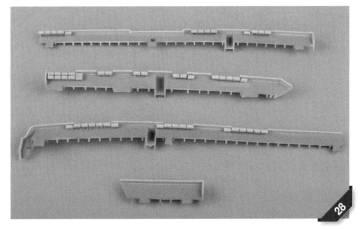

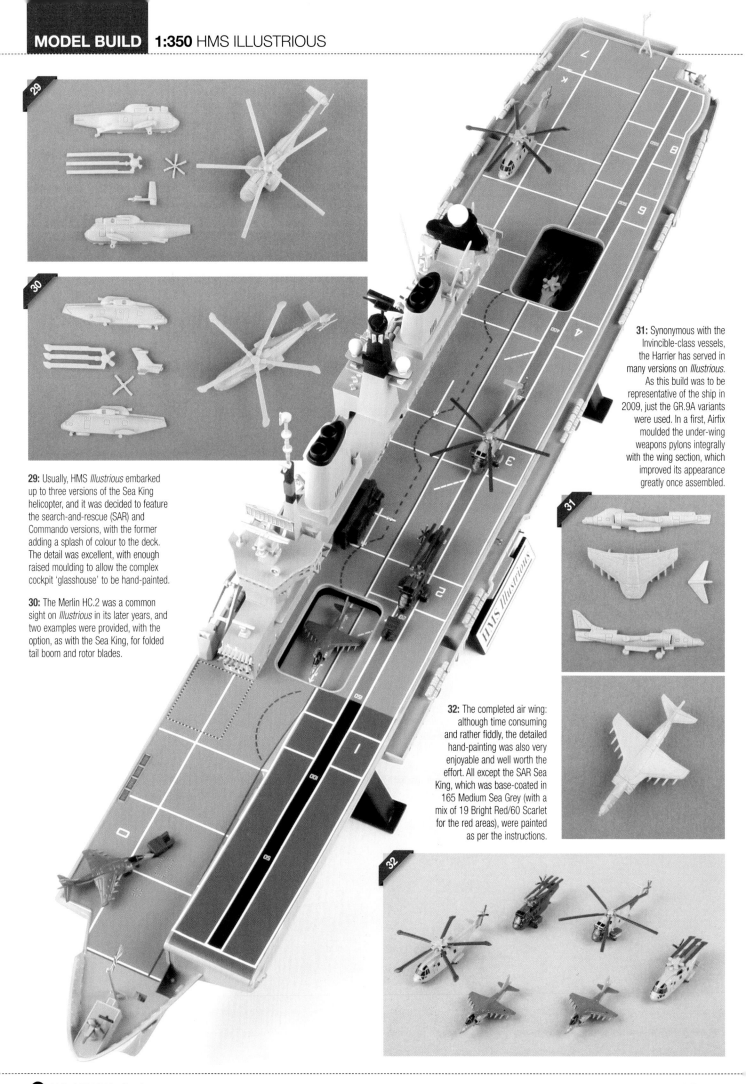

29: Usually, HMS *Illustrious* embarked up to three versions of the Sea King helicopter, and it was decided to feature the search-and-rescue (SAR) and Commando versions, with the former adding a splash of colour to the deck. The detail was excellent, with enough raised moulding to allow the complex cockpit 'glasshouse' to be hand-painted.

30: The Merlin HC.2 was a common sight on *Illustrious* in its later years, and two examples were provided, with the option, as with the Sea King, for folded tail boom and rotor blades.

31: Synonymous with the Invincible-class vessels, the Harrier has served in many versions on *Illustrious*. As this build was to be representative of the ship in 2009, just the GR.9A variants were used. In a first, Airfix moulded the under-wing weapons pylons integrally with the wing section, which improved its appearance greatly once assembled.

32: The completed air wing: although time consuming and rather fiddly, the detailed hand-painting was also very enjoyable and well worth the effort. All except the SAR Sea King, which was base-coated in 165 Medium Sea Grey (with a mix of 19 Bright Red/60 Scarlet for the red areas), were painted as per the instructions.

33: No carrier deck is complete without the various cranes and tow-trucks that enable operations to take place, and Airfix provided two towing tractors and a single boom-crane. Painting was minimal, with all three coloured 163 Dark Green overall and details picked out in black.

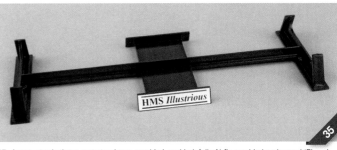

35: A very sturdy three-part stand was provided, and helpfully Airfix provided embossed 'F' and 'R' labels to ensure that it was mounted correctly under the ship. It was undercoated with light grey, and then two airbrushed layers of 21 Gloss Black were applied. The thickness of the decals paid dividends here, as there was no bleed-through of the underlying colour.

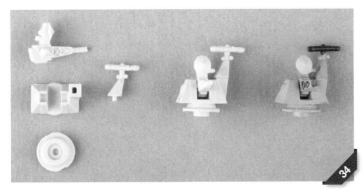

34: HMS *Illustrious*' primary self-defence capability was provided by three 30mm Goalkeeper close-in weapons systems. Three multi-part examples were provided and these were splendid assemblies, and far better than other styrene offerings. Careful painting and the application of a black/brown wash highlighted the details on the gun support lattice.

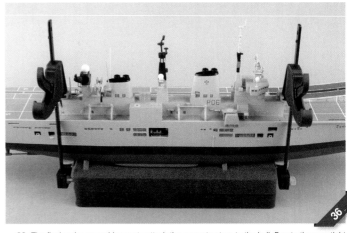

36: The final major assembly was to attach the superstructure to the hull. Due to the very tight fit between the two, the parts were clamped securely and left overnight to dry. A combination of black/brown and dark grey washes provided depth to the various grilles and vents that adorned the hull, with any seepage removed with a cotton wool bud soaked in thinners. Once dry, various smaller parts and the aircraft were added to complete the build.

"Airfix provided two towing tractors and a single boom-crane"

AIRFIX BATTLES INTRODUCTORY SET

SPRING 2016

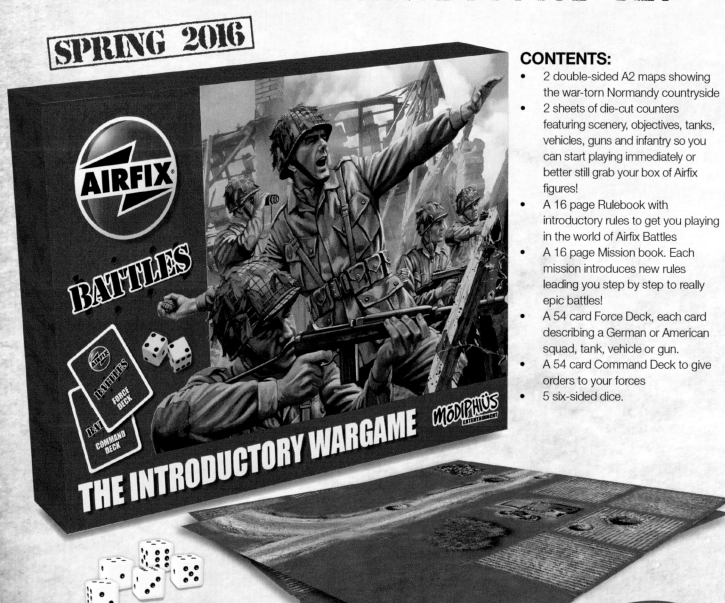

CONTENTS:

- 2 double-sided A2 maps showing the war-torn Normandy countryside
- 2 sheets of die-cut counters featuring scenery, objectives, tanks, vehicles, guns and infantry so you can start playing immediately or better still grab your box of Airfix figures!
- A 16 page Rulebook with introductory rules to get you playing in the world of Airfix Battles
- A 16 page Mission book. Each mission introduces new rules leading you step by step to really epic battles!
- A 54 card Force Deck, each card describing a German or American squad, tank, vehicle or gun.
- A 54 card Command Deck to give orders to your forces
- 5 six-sided dice.

FIND OUT MORE AT WWW.MODIPHIUS.COM/AIRFIX

A WHOLE INTRODUCTORY WARGAME RANGE!

QUICK BATTLES WITH YOUR PLASTIC SOLDIERS!

A fast and fun introductory wargame playable with all your Airfix figures and vehicles. Airfix Battles comes with everything you need to play exciting World War Two battles straight out of the box including die cut cardboard counters for tanks, infantry and guns in case you don't have any figures to hand.

AIRFIX Battles lets you plan your army using the Force Deck. Draw the cards or select the ones you need to build an exciting army to challenge your friends. Set up the battle using step by step instructions in the Mission book and you're ready to play. Each player has a hand of Command Cards to move and fight their forces, bring in airstrikes or artillery support. You'll never know what your opponent is going to do next!

AIRFIX Battles will be available in all good model stores & game shops from April 2016.

FORCE AND COMMAND DECKS

The Airfix Battles Force Deck and Command Decks will be available as a double pack to enable commanders to purchase just the Collector's Edition book and dive in to full scale battles. Each deck consists of 54 cards. Watch out for new Force Decks to expand your forces.

COLLECTOR'S EDITION

The Airfix Battles Collector's Edition introduces new rules to expand your game, as well as showing you how to move your battles to real war-games terrain with movement in inches or centimetres. The book will contain fantastic photography of games in action to inspire you as well as much bigger campaigns. The Collector's Edition will be available in print and PDF.

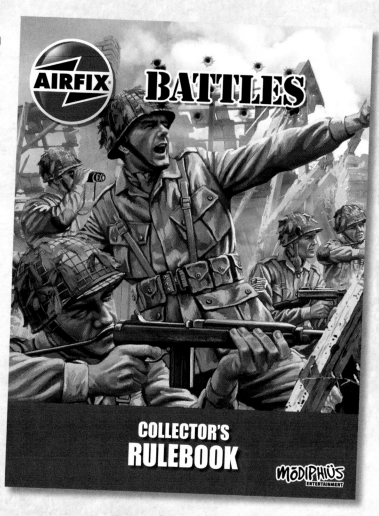

AIRFIX BATTLES

COLLECTOR'S RULEBOOK

MODIPHIUS ENTERTAINMENT

AIRFIX BATTLES FORCE DECK

AIRFIX BATTLES COMMAND DECK

AIRFIX BATTLES FORCE DECK

SUMMER 2016

MODIPHIUS ENTERTAINMENT

PRE-ORDER NOW FROM WWW.MODIPHIUS.COM/AIRFIX AND GET A SPECIAL BONUS WITH YOUR ORDER!

Quick... Get Building!

QUICK BUILD

Airfix Quick Build kits are a great way to introduce youngsters to the hobby

Standard plastic kits can be daunting for young children, but the Quick Build range is perfect for getting them used to handling and assembling parts...and they get a super toy as a result. The pre-coloured, snap-fitting pieces simply push together without glue or paint, and form into an impressive model with its own self-adhesive stickers. There are currently ten models in the range, but more will be added in 2016. From classic aircraft such as the Spitfire and Messerschmitt Bf 109, and modern Typhoon and Harrier jets, to cool Bugatti Veyron and Lamborghini Aventador supercars. Quick Build is a colourful world of construction fun for kids aged 5 and upwards.

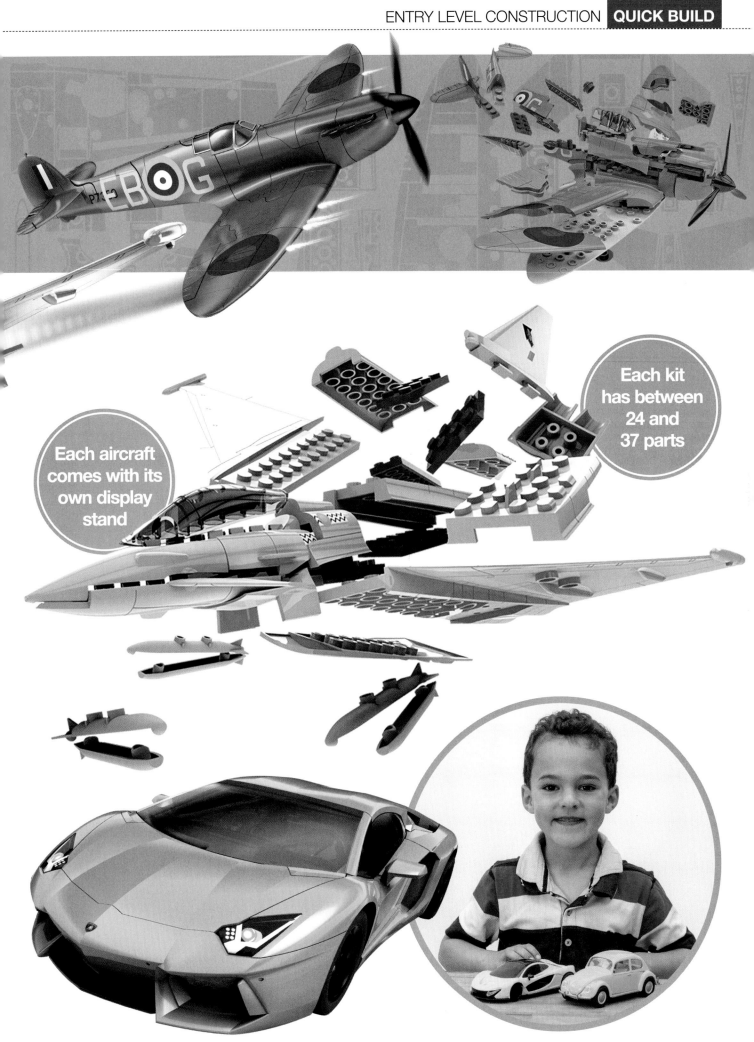

Each aircraft comes with its own display stand

Each kit has between 24 and 37 parts

Model Spec

Grumman F4F-4 Wildcat

Scale: 1:72
Stock code: A02070
Built by: Jen Wright

Gain inspiration with our gallery of Airfix models

Showcase

Model Spec

Lightning F.2A/F.6

Scale: 1:48
Stock code: A09178
Built by: Toni Canfora

Model Spec

Fairey Swordfish Mk1

Scale: 1:72
Stock code: A05006
Built by: Tony O'Toole

Model Spec

Avro Lancaster B.III (Special)

Scale: 1:72
Stock code: A09007
Built by: Jen Wright

Showcase

Model Spec

Hawker Typhoon MkIB

Scale: 1:24
Stock code: A19002
Built by: Steve Budd

Model Spec

Boulton Paul Defiant

Scale: 1:72
Stock code: A02069
Built by: Jen Wright

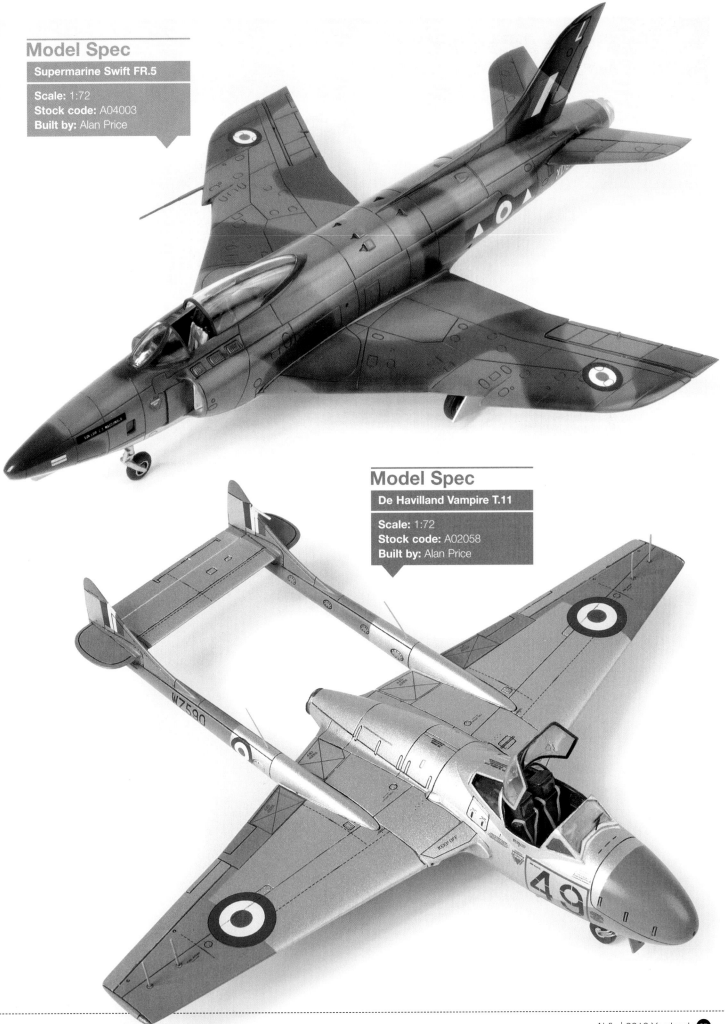

Model Spec

Supermarine Swift FR.5

Scale: 1:72
Stock code: A04003
Built by: Alan Price

Model Spec

De Havilland Vampire T.11

Scale: 1:72
Stock code: A02058
Built by: Alan Price

Showcase

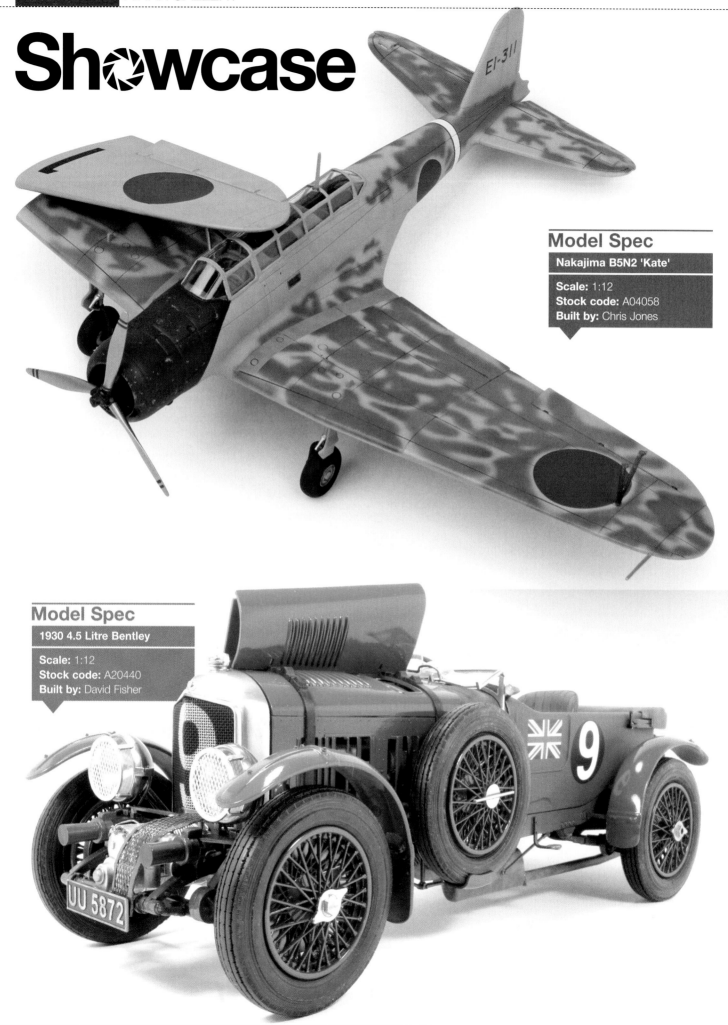

Model Spec

Nakajima B5N2 'Kate'

Scale: 1:12
Stock code: A04058
Built by: Chris Jones

Model Spec

1930 4.5 Litre Bentley

Scale: 1:12
Stock code: A20440
Built by: David Fisher

Model Spec

Heinkel He 111P-2

Scale: 1:72
Stock code: A06014
Built by: Alan Price

Model Spec

Bristol Beaufighter Mk.X

Scale: 1:72
Stock code: A04019
Built by: Jen Wright

Showcase

Model Spec

Hawker Hurricane Mk.I

Scale: 1:48
Stock code: A05127
Built by: Steve Budd

Model Spec

Douglas A-4 Skyhawk

Scale: 1:72
Stock code: A03029
Built by: Toni Canfora

Model Spec

Gloster Javelin FAW.9/9R

Scale: 1:48
Stock code: A12007
Built by: Alan Price

Model Spec

Dornier Do 17Z

Scale: 1:72
Stock code: A05010
Built by: Alan Price

Connect to Airfix

Interact with other like-minded modellers from around the world. Swap tips and ideas, enter competitions to win great prizes and get up-to-the-minute development news before anyone else!

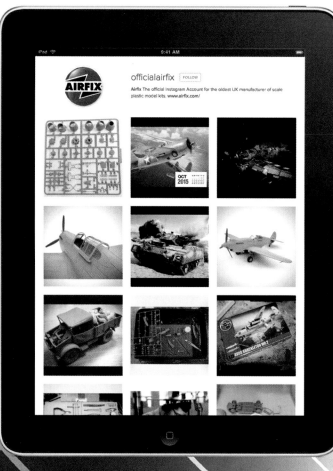

officialairfix FOLLOW

Airfix The official Instagram Account for the oldest UK manufacturer of scale plastic model kits. www.airfix.com/

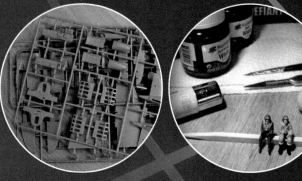

Out and About

Head on over to our YouTube channel where there are more and more videos being uploaded.

The Best of #WorkspaceWednesday

A different users' workspace is featured each week...here are a few of our favourites.

At Dover Castle

 Like us!
www.facebook.com/airfix

 Follow us!
www.twitter.com/airfix

Watch us!
www.youtube.com/officialairfix

 Share us!
www.instagram.com/officialairfix

Development Sneak Peeks!

 Our Facebook and Twitter pages are also the first place to see upcoming releases and learn more about the history of projects.

Airfix

We are really pleased to announce for 2016 the Gloster Meteor F.8 in 1/48th scale! All this and more in this week's WorkBench blog! Happy Friday!

http://www.airfix.com/uk-en/news/workbench

Airfix Workbench / News |

Airfix

AIRFIX.COM

Airfix

Remember the Design Team's #WorkspaceWednesday? They've only gone built the first shot and it's looking great! Find out more here more here:

http://www.airfix.com/.../airfix-development-news-avro-shack.../

Airfix Development News - Avro Shackleton MR2 1:72 / News | Airfix

Exciting news this week as we take you behind-the-scenes at Airfix HQ to look at the development of one of the key Airfix releases this year, the Avro Shackleton...

AIRFIX.COM

FORUM

From the Forum...

The Airfix Forum is home to a friendly and knowledgeable community, who all came together to discuss and debate plastic model kits, both old and new. Whether you are an expert or a novice, the Airfix Forum is the place to be for modelling discussion. Don't miss out on all the modelling news and become part of the community. Join the discussion over at www.airfix.com/forum

Like us!
facebook.com/airfix

Follow us!
twitter.com/airfix

Watch us!
youtube.com/officialairfix

Share us!
instagram.com/officialairfix

Brands Hatch
Beauty

Ian Hartup experiences a heady dose of nostalgia with Airfix's re-issued Ford 3 Litre GT (P68)

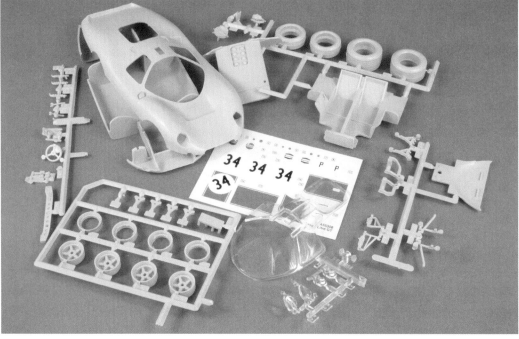

Starter Gift Set: A55308

Airfix's Ford 3 Litre GT kit dates originally to 1969, which makes it nearly as old as the author... but with care a most pleasing replica can be built.

With this re-release comes a beautifully printed and well-researched new decal sheet, and Airfix's moulds appear to have been neatened before the runners were produced. The fresh markings allow the modeller to build the car as it raced at Brands Hatch in 1968, in the BOAC 500 endurance race.

Left: The kit has a decent parts count for an older 1:32 car package. The clear parts are good and just required a quick polish before they were put to one side...and the new decal sheet is simple but very effective.

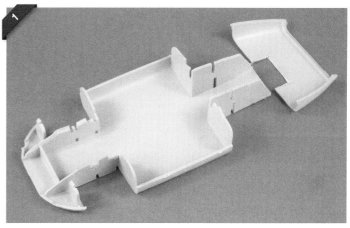

1: To enable the bodywork to be painted in the same manner as the real car, the rear valance was removed. First a razor saw was used to slice down parallel to the rear suspension mounts, before a few passes with a scalpel separated it completely.

2: The front and rear sections of the floor, which had been separated, were glued to the upper body and the centre piece dropped into place to ensure everything aligned properly. Careful fettling was required to obtain a good fit, while the raised shut lines were removed at this stage.

3: With everything loosely held in place, the beautiful shape of the P68 became apparent. There were ejector pin marks on the inside of the roof sections, and the opportunity was taken to remove them and ensure the gazing fitted properly. ➡

"The fresh markings allow the modeller to build the car as it raced at Brands Hatch in 1968"

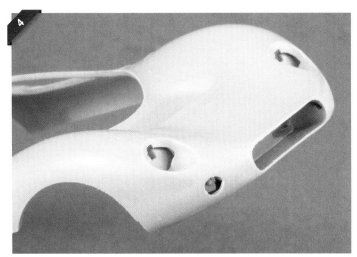

4: The front radiator inlet and the fog light housings required work to ensure their shapes remained symmetrical, after the body panel joins had been eradicated. In the end, just a few small dabs of Humbrol filler was required and then only at the rear.

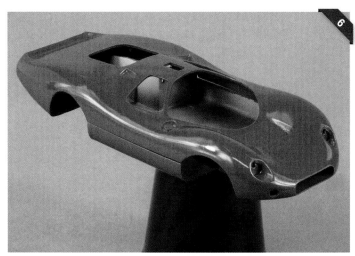

6: Humbrol 21 Enamel Red was diluted 50:50 with Cellulose thinners and sprayed onto the model in light misting coats, with a minute or two between each until even coverage was apparent. The paint was then thinned to a 25:75 ratio and a series of 'wet' coats were applied

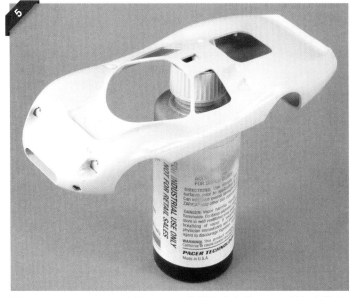

5: The body was mounted to a suitable armature with Blu-Tack...in this case an old bottle filled with lead shot was used to give a proper hand hold. The model then received grey primer ahead of the top colour.

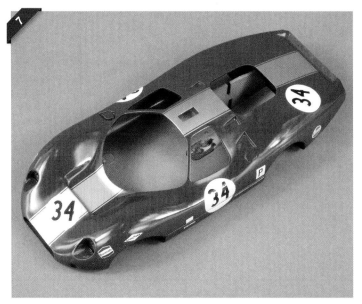

7: The paint was allowed to cure for a week and then, polished with fine compound; after the polish residue had been removed the decals were applied. A hairdryer was utilised to bed the decals into place properly, as the use of decal solvents could potentially damage the gloss finish.

8: A coat of Humbrol Gloss Acrylic Varnish was applied to seal the decals and paintwork. This was added with a broad, flat brush to ensure good coverage.

9: A thinned black wash added depth to the area around the fuel filler cap—the silver cap would be painted at a later stage, but in general the car really looked the part by this stage.

10: The main glazing was fitted, but beforehand the internal framing was painted with Humbrol 85 Coal Black. Remember to drill out the hole for the roof-mounted rear view mirror!

11: The headlight lens covers were edged in black, and the lenses of the light in silver, before they were assembled with a dab of PVA...all that was required to hold them in place. ➜

"Humbrol Gloss Acrylic Varnish was applied to seal the decals and paintwork"

12: The front and rear suspension units are mostly hidden from view on the finished model. They were built quickly with liquid cement and left to dry overnight. Care was required to ensure they all aligned correctly.

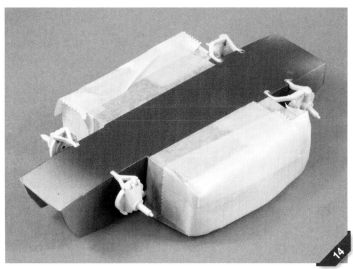

14: Careful masking was required to protect the decaled areas. The interior and under surfaces were sanded gently with fine grade abrasive paper, to ensure the paint would adhere to the polished bodywork.

13: A venerable bottle of Humbrol Clearfix was brought into service to help glaze the fog light housings, as the small plastic parts were deemed simply not clear enough. The light openings actually have lenses moulded in place, and these were picked out with silver paint.

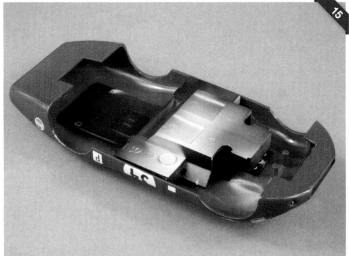

15: The pre-prepared interior was fixed into the upper body shell. The kit provided neat and positive fixings for the main tub, although the location for the instrument panel was less intuitive and requiring some gentle jiggling to position it correctly.

"Humbrol Clearfix was brought into service to help glaze the fog light housing"

16: With the interior in place the model began to look some way towards being complete. Note the painted fuel filler and intake grilles on the rear deck.

17: The lower bodywork was unsheathed from its masking and the radiator painted silver, but at some point the lower section had begun to exhibit a slight twist.

18: The lower bodywork was fitted to the upper section and a hint of PVA white glue ensured it all stayed in place. Berna Clamps secured everything while drying.

19: The wheels had been sprayed with silver at the same time as the radiator, and the spokes were now picked out with Humbrol Red to match the bodywork. Once this had dried, a black wash added depth behind the spokes before the wheels and kick-offs were fixed with more PVA.

Airfix Index

Full kit listings and stock codes

English Electric Lightning F.2A
(A04054)

Series 1 Aircraft

Code	Product Description	Scale
A01086	FOKKER E.II EINDECKER	1:72
A01004	N.A. P-51D MUSTANG	1:72
A01006	FOLLAND GNAT	1:72
A01008	MESSERSCHMITT BF 109E	1:72
A01010	HAWKER HURRICANE MK.I	1:72
A01020	FOCKE WULF FW 190A-8	1:72
A01025	DH TIGER MOTH MILITARY	1:72
A01071A	SUPERMARINE SPITFIRE MK.IA	1:72
A01005	MITSUBISHI ZERO A6M2B	1:72
A01003	CURTIS P-40B TOMAHAWK	1:72

Code	Product Description	Scale
A02074	GRUMMAN MARTLET	1:72
A02102	SUPERMARINE SPITFIRE MK.VA	1:72
A02005C	RED ARROWS HAWK 2015 SCHEME	1:72
A02017	SUPERMARINE SPITFIRE PR.XIX	1:72
A02029A	MESSERSCHMITT BF 109G	1:72
A02041	HAWKER TYPHOON 1B	1:72
A02047	F-51 MUSTANG	1:72
A02052	GLOSTER GLADIATOR	1:72
A02058	D.H. VAMPIRE T.11	1:72
A02065A	SUPERMARINE SPITFIRE MK.IXC	1:72
A02066	FOCKE WULF FW 190A-8/F-8	1:72
A02067	HAWKER HURRICANE MK.I PRE-WAR	1:72
A02069	BOULTON PAUL DEFIANT	1:72
A02070	GRUMMAN WILDCAT F4F-4	1:72

Series 2 Aircraft

Code	Product Description	Scale
A02101	ROYAL AIRCRAFT FACILITY BE2C	1:72
A02103	BAC JET PROVOST T.3	1:72

Series 3 Aircraft

Code	Product Description	Scale
A03003	BAE HARRIER GR.1	1:72

A03019	DE HAVILLAND MOSQUITO	1:72
A03029	DOUGLAS A-4 SKYHAWK	1:72
A03080	MESSERSCHMITT BF 110C/D	1:72
A03082A	SABRE F-86F	1:72
A03087	JUNKERS JU 87B-1 STUKA	1:72
A03171	VICKERS VANGUARD	1:144

A04054	ENGLISH ELECTRIC LIGHTNING F.2A	1:72
A04055	BAE HARRIER GR.3	1:72
A04056	WESTLAND SEA KING HC.4	1:72
A04057	HARRIER AV-8A	1:72
A04058	NAKAJIMA B5N2 KATE	1:72
A04176	D.H.COMET 4B	1:144

Series 4 Aircraft

Code	Product Description	Scale
A04060	NAKAJIMA B5N1 "KATE"	1:72
A04059	BISTOL BLENHEIM MK.IF	1:72
A04003	SUPERMARINE SWIFT	1:72
A04017	BRISTOL BLENHEIM MK.IV(FIGHTER)	1:72
A04019	BRISTOL BEAUFIGHTER MK.X	1:72
A04050	HARRIER GR.9	1:72
A04053	FAIREY SWORDFISH	1:72

Series 5 Aircraft

Code	Product Description	Scale
A05130	CURTISS P-40B	1:48
A05128	BOULTON PAUL DEFIANT MK.I	1:48
A05043	BRISTOL BEAUFIGHTER MK.X (LATE)	1:72
A05129	HAWKER HURRICANE MK.I - TROPICAL	1:48
A05010	DORNIER DO 17Z	1:72
A05042	E E LIGHTNING F.6	1:72
A05119	SUPERMARINE SPITFIRE PR.XIX	1:48

Boulton Paul Defiant Mk.1
(A02069)

De Havilland Mosquito FB.VI
(A25001A)

A06007	HANDLEY PAGE 0/400	1:72
A06008A	HANDLEY PAGE HALIFAX B MK.III	1:72
A06014	HEINKEL HE IIIP-2	1:72

Series 7 Aircraft

Code	Product Description	Scale
A07007	HEINKEL HE 111H-6	
A07112	DH MOSQUITO B MK.XVI	1:48

A05120A	MESSERSCHMITT BF 109E	1:48
A05123	FOLLAND GNAT	1:48
A05124	FOLLAND GNAT RED ARROWS	1:48
A05125	SUPERMARINE SPITFIRE MK.VB	1:48
A05126	SUPERMARINE SPITFIRE MK.I	1:48
A05127	HAWKER HURRICANE MK.I	1:48
A05171	BOEING 707	1:144

Series 8 Aircraft

Code	Product Description	Scale
A08017	BOEING B-17G	1:72
A08013	LANCASTER B.I/B.III	1:72
A08014	DOUGLAS DAKOTA MILITARY	1:72
A08015	DOUGLAS DAKOTA CIVIL	1:72
A08016	ARMSTRONG WHITWORTH WHITLEY MK.V	1:72

Series 6 Aircraft

Code	Product Description	Scale
A07114	JUNKERS JU 87B-1	1:48
A06001	SHORT SUNDERLAND	1:72

Series 9 Aircraft

Code	Product Description	Scale
A09182	GLOSTER METEOR F.8	1:48
A09009	ARMSTRONG WHITWORTH WHITLEY MK.VII	1:72

Ford 3LT GT
(A55308)

King Tiger Tank
(A55303)

A09007	DAMBUSTER LANCASTER	1:72
A09008	DOUGLAS DAKOTA MK.III WITH WILLYS JEEP	1:72
A09179	ENGLISH ELECTRIC LIGHTNING F.1/F.1A/ F2/F.3	1:48

Series 10 Aircraft

Code	Product Description	Scale
A10101A	ENGLISH ELECTRIC CANBERRA B.2/B.20	1:48

Series 11 Aircraft

Code	Product Description	Scale
A11004	AVRO SHACKLETON MR.2	1:72

Series 12 Aircraft

Code	Product Description	Scale
A12008	HANDLEY PAGE VICTOR B.2	1:72
A12001A	SUPERMARINE SPITFIRE	1:24

| A12002A | MESSERSCHMITT BF 109E | 1:24 |

Series 14 Aircraft

Code	Product Description	Scale
A14002A	HURRICANE MK.I	1:24
A14003A	MUSTANG P-51K	1:24

Series 16 Aircraft

Code	Product Description	Scale
A16001A	FOCKE WULFE FW 190A	1:24

Series 18 Aircraft

Code	Product Description	Scale
A18002A	JU 87B STUKA	1:24

Series 19 Aircraft

Code	Product Description	Scale
A19003	HAWKER TYPHOON MK.IB - CAR DOOR	1:24

Bristol Beaufighter Mk.X
(A04019)

Series 25 Aircraft

Code	Product Description	Scale
A25001A	**MOSQUITO FB.VI**	1:24

Cars

Code	Product Description	Scale
A03413	**FORD FIESTA WRC**	1:32
A03414	**BMW MINI COUNTRYMAN WRC**	1:32

Warships/Boats

Code	Product Description	Scale
A05281	**RAF RESCUE LAUNCH**	1:72
A07280	**RNLI SEVERN CLASS LIFEBOAT**	1:72
A14201	**HMS ILLUSTRIOUS**	1:350
A04212	**HMS BELFAST**	1:600

Classic Ships

Code	Product Description	Scale
A04207	**RMS MAURETANIA**	1:600
A06201	**RMS QUEEN ELIZABETH 1**	1:600

Air Sea Rescue Launch
(A05281)

Classic Cars And Vehicles

Code	Product Description	Scale
A20440	**BENTLEY 1930 4.5L SUPERCHARGED**	1:12
A06443	**B TYPE OMINBUS**	1:32

Series 1 Military Vehicles

Code	Product Description	Scale
A01302	**PANTHER TANK**	1:76
A01303	**SHERMAN M4 MK.I TANK**	1:76
A01304	**CHURCHILL MK.VII**	1:76
A01305	**25 PDR FIELD GUN + QUAD**	1:76
A01308	**TIGER TANK**	1:76
A01309	**BREN GUN CARRIER**	1:76
A01314	**MATADOR & 55 GUN**	1:76
A01315	**WWI 'MALE' TANK**	1:76
A01317	**LEE/GRANT TANK**	1:76
A01318	**MATILDA TANK**	1:76

Series 2 Military Vehicles

Code	Product Description	Scale
A02302	**BUFFALO AMPHIBIAN & JEEP**	1:76
A02303	**88MM GUN & TRACTOR**	1:76
A02308	**PANZER IV TANK**	1:76
A02314	**BOFORS GUN + TRACTOR**	1:76
A02315	**PAK 40 ANTI-TANK GUN & TRUCK**	1:76
A02324	**LWB LANDROVER (HD/TOP)+GS TRAILER**	1:76
A02337	**WWI 'FEMALE' TANK**	1:76
A02338	**CROMWELL CRUISER TANK**	1:76
A02339	**WILLYS JEEP TRAILER & HOWITZER**	1:72
A02340	**HIGGINS LCVP**	1:72

Series 3 Military Vehicles

Code	Product Description	Scale
A03301	**LCM MK.III & SHERMAN**	1:76

Avro Shackleton MR.2
(A11004)

Nakajima B5N1 'Kate'
(A04058)

A03306	**BEDFORD QT V1**	1:76
A03310	**KING TIGER TANK**	1:76
A03311	**TILLY & BEDFORD TRUCK**	1:76

A03312	**ALBION AM463 3 POINT FUELLER**	1:48
A03313	**BEDFORD MWD LIGHT TRUCK**	1:48

1:48 WWII Diorama Subjects

Code	Product Description	Scale
A04702	**WWII RAF GROUND CREW**	1:48

Higgins LCVP
(A02340)

1:32 Military Vehicles And Diorama Buildings

Code	Product Description	Scale
A06361	**17 PDR ANTI-TANK GUN**	1:32
A06382	**BAMBOO HOUSE**	1:32
A06383	**FRONTIER CHECKPOINT**	1:32
A08360	**CRUSADER MK.III TANK**	1:32

Diorama and Buildings

Code	Product Description	Scale
A06304	**USAAF 8TH AIRFORCE BOMBER RE-SUPPLY SET**	1:72
A03302	**RAF REFUELLING SET**	1:72
A03304	**RAF EMERGENCY SET**	1:72

17 Pdr Anti-Tank Gun
(A06361)

A03305	**RAF RECOVERY SET**	1:72
A03380	**RAF CONTROL TOWER**	1:72
A05330	**BOMBER RE-SUPPLY SET**	1:72

Series 1 Figures

Code	Product Description	Scale
A01705	**WWII GERMAN INFANTRY**	1:72

A01709	**8TH ARMY**	1:72
A01711	**AFRICA CORPS**	1:72
A01716	**WWII US MARINES**	1:72
A01717	**RUSSIAN INFANTRY**	1:72
A01718	**JAPANESE INFANTRY**	1:72
A01723	**BRITISH PARATROOPS**	1:72
A01726	**WWI GERMAN INFANTRY**	1:72
A01727	**WWI BRITISH INFANTRY**	1:72
A01728	**WWI FRENCH INFANTRY**	1:72
A01729	**WWI AMERICAN INFANTRY**	1:72
A01731	**WWI ROYAL HORSE ARTILLERY**	1:72
A01732	**BRITISH COMMANDOS**	1:72
A01747	**RAF PERSONNEL**	1:72
A01750	**AUSTRALIAN INFANTRY**	1:72
A01751	**US PARATROOPS**	1:72
A01753	**GERMAN PARATROOPS**	1:72
A01763	**WWII BRITISH INFANTRY N.EUROPE**	1:72

Battle of Britain - 75th Anniversary
(A50173)

Series 2 Figures

Code	Product Description	Scale
A02701	**BRITISH PARATROOPS**	1:72
A02702	**GERMAN INFANTRY**	1:72
A02703	**US INFANTRY**	1:72
A02705	**BRITISH COMMANDOS**	1:72
A02708	**AFRIKA KORPS**	1:72
A02711	**US PARATROOPS**	1:72
A02712	**GERMAN PARATROOPS**	1:72
A02718	**BRITISH INFANTRY WWII**	1:72

Series 4 Figures

Code	Product Description	Scale
A04710	**WWII BRITISH INFANTRY SUPPORT SET**	1:72
A04713	**WWII GERMAN MOUNTAIN TROOPS**	1:72

Airfix Accessories

Code	Product Description	Scale
AF1004	**ELECTRIC MOTOR**	N/A
AF1008	**ASSORTED SMALL STANDS**	N/A

Small Starter Gift Sets

Code	Product Description	Scale
A55100	**SUPERMARINE SPITFIRE MK.IA**	1:72
A55104	**HMS VICTORY**	FTB
A55105	**RED ARROWS GNAT**	1:72
A55106	**MESSERSCHMITT BF 109E-3**	1:72
A55107	**NORTH AMERICAN P-51D MUSTANG™**	1:72

Bomber Re-Supply Set
(A05330)

RAF Emergency Set
(A03304)

| A55111 | **HAWKER HURRICANE MK.I** | 1:72 |
| A55109 | **CROMWELL CRUISER TANK** | 1:76 |

Medium Starter Gift Sets

Code	Product Description	Scale
A50089A	**ASTON MARTIN DB5 - SILVER**	1:32
A55202B	**RED ARROWS HAWK 2015**	1:72
A55201	**TRIUMPH HERALD**	1:32
A55203	**DOUGLAS A-4 SKYHAWK**	1:72
A55204	**DE HAVILLAND VAMPIRE T.11**	1:72
A55205	**HAWKER HARRIER GR.1**	1:72
A55207	**VW BEETLE**	1:32
A55208	**HAWKER TYPHOON MK.IB**	1:72
A55210	**GERMAN INFANTRY MULTI-POSE**	1:32
A55211	**WWII BRITISH INFANTRY MULTIPOSE GIFT SET**	1:32
A55212	**WWII U.S. INFANTRY MULTIPOSE GIFT SET**	1:32
A55213	**STARTER SET BOULTON PAUL DEFIANT**	1:72
A55214	**STARTER SET GRUMMAN WILDCAT F4F-4**	1:72
A55303	**KING TIGER TANK**	1:76

Large Starter Gift Sets - Aircraft

Code	Product Description	Scale
A55307	**WESTLAND SEA KING HAR.3**	1:72

A50098	**EUROFIGHTER TYPHOON**	1:72
A55300	**BAE HARRIER GR.9**	1:72
A55305	**ENGLISH ELECTRIC LIGHTNING F.2A**	1:72

Large Starter & Gift Sets - Cars

Code	Product Description	Scale
A50110	**ASTON MARTIN DBR9 GULF**	1:32
A50125	**MINI COOPER S**	1:32
A55302	**FORD FIESTA RS WRC**	1:32
A55304	**MINI COUNTRYMAN WRC**	1:32
A55306	**JAGUAR XKRGT3 'FANTASY SCHEME'**	1:32
A55308	**STARTER SET FORD 3 LITRE GT**	1:32
A55309	**STARTER SET MASERATI INDY**	1:32

Boxed Gift Sets

Code	Product Description	Scale
A50177	**FOKKER E.II/BE2C DOGFIGHT DOUBLE**	1:72
A50179	**JU 87/GLOSTER GLADIATOR DOGFIGHT DOUBLE**	1:72

A50180	**PEARL HARBOR - 75TH ANNIVERSARY GIRFT SET**	1:72
A50135	**SUPERMARINE SPITFIRE MK.IA MESSERSCHMITT BF 109E-4**	1:72
A50160	**SUPERMARINE SPITFIRE MK.VB MESSERSCHMITT BF 109E**	1:48
A50169	**DOGFIGHT DOUBLE B5N KATE/WILDCAT F4F-4**	1:72
A50170	**DOGFIGHT DOUBLE DEFIANT/DORNIER**	1:72
A50171	**DOGFIGHT DOUBLE BEAUFIGHTER/FW 190A-8**	1:72

WWI Gift Sets

Code	Product Description	Scale
A50163	**WWI OLD BILL BUS**	1:32
A50178	**BATTLE OF THE SOMME CENTENARY GIFT SET**	1:72

Battle Of Britain Gift Sets

Code	Product Description	Scale
A50172	**BATTLE OF BRITAIN READY FOR BATTLE SET 1:48**	1:48

Fokker E.II/Be2c Dogfight Double
(A50177)

Supermarine Spitfire Mk.vb
Messerschmitt Bf 109E
(A50160)

A50173	**BATTLE OF BRITAIN 75TH ANNIVERSARY SET 1:72**	1:72

D-Day Gift Sets

Code	Product Description	Scale
A50009	**D-DAY BATTLEFRONT GIFT SET**	1:72
A50156	**D-DAY SEA ASSAULT GIFT SET**	1:72
A50157	**D-DAY AIR ASSAULT GIFT SET**	1:72
A50162	**D-DAY OPERATION OVERLORD GIANT GIFT SET**	1:72

Themed Diorama Sets

Code	Product Description	Scale
A50015	**RAF BATTLE OF BRITAIN AIRFIELD SET**	1:72
A50097	**AVRO VULCAN GIFT SET**	1:72
A50138	**DAMBUSTERS GIFT SET**	1:72

Battle Of Britain Memorial Flight

Code	Product Description	Scale
A50158	**BBMF COLLECTION**	1:72

Imperial War Musuem

Code	Product Description	Scale
A50069	**HMS BELFAST**	1:600

Royal Navy

Code	Product Description	Scale
A50059	**HMS ILLUSTRIOUS GIFT SET**	1:350

Ships And Tourist

Code	Product Description	Scale
A50045	**CUTTY SARK**	1:130
A50046	**GOLDEN HIND**	1:72

1930 Bentley 4.5 Litre
(A20440)

| A50049 | **HMS VICTORY** | 1:180 |
| A50164 | **RMS TITANIC** | 1:700 |

Airfix Engineer

Code	Product Description	Scale
A20005	**JET ENGINE**	N/A
A42509	**INTERNAL COMBUSTION ENGINE**	N/A

Westland Sea King HC.4
(A04056)

Airfix Quick Build Aircraft

Code	Product Description	Scale
J6000	**SPITFIRE QUICK BUILD**	FTB
J6001	**MESSERSCHMITT BF 109E QUICK BUILD**	FTB
J6002	**EUROFIGHTER TYPHOON QUICK BUILD**	FTB
J6003	**BAE HAWK QUICK BUILD**	FTB
J6016	**P-51D MUSTANG QUICK BUILD**	FTB
J6009	**HARRIER QUICKBUILD**	FTB

Airfix Quick Build Cars

Code	Product Description	Scale
J6007	**LAMBORGHINI AVENTADOR QUICKBUILD**	FTB
J6008	**BUGATTI VEYRON QUICKBUILD**	FTB
J6013	**MCLAREN P1**	FTB
J6015	**VW BEETLE**	FTB

The Engineer and Quick Build range will be extending late 2016.

Licence Acknowledgement

Mini Countryman WRC
(A03414)

Turn your model kit into a masterpiece with...

Humbrol™
Paints & Accessories

Over 60% of the Humbrol range
is now made in the UK

Humbrol™ Enamel Paints

Matt Colours 14ml

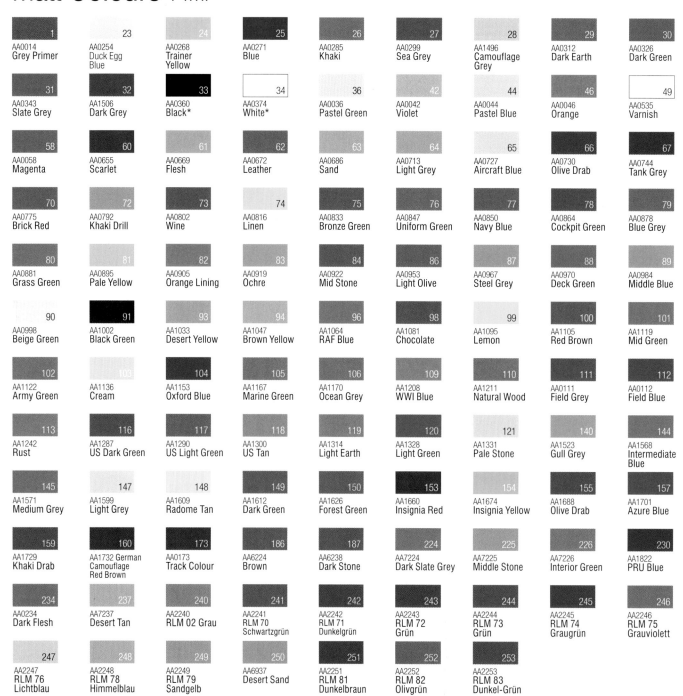

No.	Code	Name
1	AA0014	Grey Primer
23	AA0254	Duck Egg Blue
24	AA0268	Trainer Yellow
25	AA0271	Blue
26	AA0285	Khaki
27	AA0299	Sea Grey
28	AA1496	Camouflage Grey
29	AA0312	Dark Earth
30	AA0326	Dark Green
31	AA0343	Slate Grey
32	AA1506	Dark Grey
33	AA0360	Black*
34	AA0374	White*
36	AA0036	Pastel Green
42	AA0042	Violet
44	AA0044	Pastel Blue
46	AA0046	Orange
49	AA0535	Varnish
58	AA0058	Magenta
60	AA0655	Scarlet
61	AA0669	Flesh
62	AA0672	Leather
63	AA0686	Sand
64	AA0713	Light Grey
65	AA0727	Aircraft Blue
66	AA0730	Olive Drab
67	AA0744	Tank Grey
70	AA0775	Brick Red
72	AA0792	Khaki Drill
73	AA0802	Wine
74	AA0816	Linen
75	AA0833	Bronze Green
76	AA0847	Uniform Green
77	AA0850	Navy Blue
78	AA0864	Cockpit Green
79	AA0878	Blue Grey
80	AA0881	Grass Green
81	AA0895	Pale Yellow
82	AA0905	Orange Lining
83	AA0919	Ochre
84	AA0922	Mid Stone
86	AA0953	Light Olive
87	AA0967	Steel Grey
88	AA0970	Deck Green
89	AA0984	Middle Blue
90	AA0998	Beige Green
91	AA1002	Black Green
93	AA1033	Desert Yellow
94	AA1047	Brown Yellow
96	AA1064	RAF Blue
98	AA1081	Chocolate
99	AA1095	Lemon
100	AA1105	Red Brown
101	AA1119	Mid Green
102	AA1122	Army Green
103	AA1136	Cream
104	AA1153	Oxford Blue
105	AA1167	Marine Green
106	AA1170	Ocean Grey
109	AA1208	WWI Blue
110	AA1211	Natural Wood
111	AA0111	Field Grey
112	AA0112	Field Blue
113	AA1242	Rust
116	AA1287	US Dark Green
117	AA1290	US Light Green
118	AA1300	US Tan
119	AA1314	Light Earth
120	AA1328	Light Green
121	AA1331	Pale Stone
140	AA1523	Gull Grey
144	AA1568	Intermediate Blue
145	AA1571	Medium Grey
147	AA1599	Light Grey
148	AA1609	Radome Tan
149	AA1612	Dark Green
150	AA1626	Forest Green
153	AA1660	Insignia Red
154	AA1674	Insignia Yellow
155	AA1688	Olive Drab
157	AA1701	Azure Blue
159	AA1729	Khaki Drab
160	AA1732	German Camouflage Red Brown
173	AA0173	Track Colour
186	AA6224	Brown
187	AA6238	Dark Stone
224	AA7224	Dark Slate Grey
225	AA7225	Middle Stone
226	AA7226	Interior Green
230	AA1822	PRU Blue
234	AA0234	Dark Flesh
237	AA7237	Desert Tan
240	AA2240	RLM 02 Grau
241	AA2241	RLM 70 Schwartzgrün
242	AA2242	RLM 71 Dunkelgrün
243	AA2243	RLM 72 Grün
244	AA2244	RLM 73 Grün
245	AA2245	RLM 74 Graugrün
246	AA2246	RLM 75 Grauviolett
247	AA2247	RLM 76 Lichtblau
248	AA2248	RLM 78 Himmelblau
249	AA2249	RLM 79 Sandgelb
250	AA6937	Desert Sand
251	AA2251	RLM 81 Dunkelbraun
252	AA2252	RLM 82 Olivgrün
253	AA2253	RLM 83 Dunkel-Grün

*Also available in 50ml (No.2) tinlets.

Humbrol enamel paint has been the modeller's standard for decades. This superb paint can also be used as an art and craft paint on many different surfaces, both indoors and outdoors.

 Follow us! www.twitter.com/humbrol

 Like us! www.facebook.com/humbrol

 Watch us! www.youtube.com/humbrol

Satin Colours 14ml

71	85	123	125	126	127	128	129	130
AA0789 Oak	AA0936 Coal Black	AA1359 Extra Dark Sea Grey	AA1376 US Dark Grey	AA1393 US Medium Grey	AA1403 US Ghost Grey	AA1417 US Compass Grey	AA1420 US Gull Grey	AA1434 White

131	132	133	135	156	163	164	165	166
AA1448 Mid Green	AA1451 Red	AA1465 Brown	AA1482 Varnish	AA1691 Dark Camouflage Grey	AA1777 Dark Green	AA1780 Dark Sea Grey	AA1794 Medium Sea Grey	AA1804 Light Aircraft Grey

167	168	174	195	196
AA1818 RAF Barley Grey	AA1821 Hemp	AA1897 Signal Red	AA6330 Dark Green	AA6344 Light Grey

Gloss Colours 14ml

2	3	5	7	9	10	14	15	18
AA0028 Emerald*	AA0031 Brunswick Green*	AA0059 Dark Admiralty	AA0076 Light Buff	AA0103 Tan	AA0117 Service Brown	AA0151 French Blue*	AA0165 Midnight Blue*	AA0196 Orange*

19	20	21	22	35	38	40	41	47
AA0206 Bright Red*	AA0223 Crimson*	AA0237 Black*	AA0240 White*	AA0388 Varnish*	AA0415 Lime	AA0432 Pale Grey	AA0446 Ivory	AA0518 Sea Blue

48	68	69	??	208	209	220	238	239
AA0521 Mediterranean Blue	AA0758 Purple	AA0761 Yellow*	AA6389 Pink	AA7081 Fluorescent Signal Green	AA7105 Fluorescent Fire Orange	AA6608 Italian Red	AA0238 Arrow Red	AA0239 British Racing Green

Metallic Colours 14ml

11	12	16	50	51	52	53	54	55
AA0120 Silver*	AA0134 Copper	AA0179 Gold	AA0549 Green Mist	AA0552 Sunset Red	AA0566 Baltic Blue	AA0583 Gunmetal	AA0597 Brass	AA0607 Bronze

56	171	191	201	222
AA0610 Aluminium	AA1852 Antique Bronze	AA6272 Chrome Silver	AA6392 Metallic Black	Moonlight Blue

Metalcote Colours 14ml

27001	27002	27003	27004
AC5008 Aluminium	AC5011 Polished Aluminium	AC5025 Polished Steel	AC5039 Gunmetal

Clear Colours 14ml

1321	1322	1325
AC6027 Red	AC6030 Orange	AC6061 Green

Humbrol Enamel 14 ml ℮

HUMBROL EVOCO AG4000
HUMBROL EVOCO AG4000

Turn your model kit into a masterpiece!

Made in the UK

Humbrol™ Acrylic Paints

Matt Colours 14ml

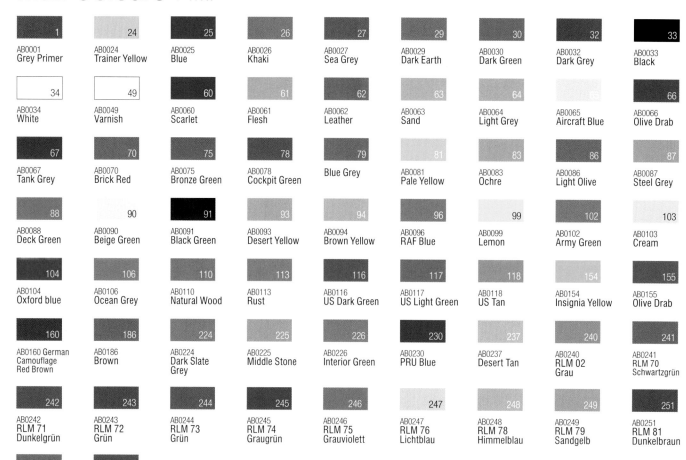

1 AB0001 Grey Primer	**24** AB0024 Trainer Yellow	**25** AB0025 Blue	**26** AB0026 Khaki	**27** AB0027 Sea Grey	**29** AB0029 Dark Earth	**30** AB0030 Dark Green	**32** AB0032 Dark Grey	**33** AB0033 Black
34 AB0034 White	**49** AB0049 Varnish	**60** AB0060 Scarlet	**61** AB0061 Flesh	**62** AB0062 Leather	**63** AB0063 Sand	**64** AB0064 Light Grey	**65** AB0065 Aircraft Blue	**66** AB0066 Olive Drab
67 AB0067 Tank Grey	**70** AB0070 Brick Red	**75** AB0075 Bronze Green	**78** AB0078 Cockpit Green	**79** Blue Grey	**81** AB0081 Pale Yellow	**83** AB0083 Ochre	**86** AB0086 Light Olive	**87** AB0087 Steel Grey
88 AB0088 Deck Green	**90** AB0090 Beige Green	**91** AB0091 Black Green	**93** AB0093 Desert Yellow	**94** AB0094 Brown Yellow	**96** AB0096 RAF Blue	**99** AB0099 Lemon	**102** AB0102 Army Green	**103** AB0103 Cream
104 AB0104 Oxford blue	**106** AB0106 Ocean Grey	**110** AB0110 Natural Wood	**113** AB0113 Rust	**116** AB0116 US Dark Green	**117** AB0117 US Light Green	**118** AB0118 US Tan	**154** AB0154 Insignia Yellow	**155** AB0155 Olive Drab
160 AB0160 German Camouflage Red Brown	**186** AB0186 Brown	**224** AB0224 Dark Slate Grey	**225** AB0225 Middle Stone	**226** AB0226 Interior Green	**230** AB0230 PRU Blue	**237** AB0237 Desert Tan	**240** AB0240 RLM 02 Grau	**241** AB0241 RLM 70 Schwartzgrün
242 AB0242 RLM 71 Dunkelgrün	**243** AB0243 RLM 72 Grün	**244** AB0244 RLM 73 Grün	**245** AB0245 RLM 74 Graugrün	**246** AB0246 RLM 75 Grauviolett	**247** AB0247 RLM 76 Lichtblau	**248** AB0248 RLM 78 Himmelblau	**249** AB0249 RLM 79 Sandgelb	**251** AB0251 RLM 81 Dunkelbraun
252 AB0252 RLM 82 Olivgrün	**253** AB0253 RLM83 Dunkel-Grün							

Satin Colours 14ml

196 AB0196 Light Grey

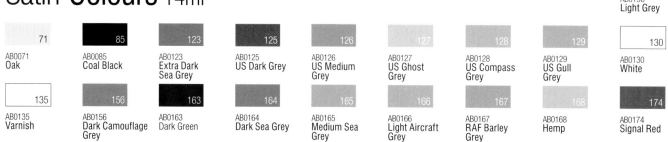

71 AB0071 Oak	**85** AB0085 Coal Black	**123** AB0123 Extra Dark Sea Grey	**125** AB0125 US Dark Grey	**126** AB0126 US Medium Grey	**127** AB0127 US Ghost Grey	**128** AB0128 US Compass Grey	**129** AB0129 US Gull Grey	**130** AB0130 White
135 AB0135 Varnish	**156** AB0156 Dark Camouflage Grey	**163** AB0163 Dark Green	**164** AB0164 Dark Sea Grey	**165** AB0165 Medium Sea Grey	**166** AB0166 Light Aircraft Grey	**167** AB0167 RAF Barley Grey	**168** AB0168 Hemp	**174** AB0174 Signal Red

The Humbrol Acrylic range has increased to more than 100 colours, and will satisfy almost every modeller's needs. Being water-based it's easy to apply by brush, which can then be cleaned with water, or by airbrush, thinned with water or a small amount of Acrylic Thinners, depending on personal preference. The paint is hard wearing and can be used on most surfaces, both indoors and outdoors.

 Follow us! www.twitter.com/humbrol

 Like us! www.facebook.com/humbrol

 Watch us! www.youtube.com/humbrol

Gloss **Colours** 14ml

2 AB0002 Emerald	**3** AB0003 Brunswick Green	**9** AB0009 Tan	**10** AB0010 Service Brown	**14** AB0014 French Blue

15 AB0015 Midnight Blue | **18** AB0018 Orange | **19** AB0019 Bright Red | **20** AB0020 Crimson

21 AB0021 Black — **22** AB0022 White — **35** AB0035 Varnish — **38** AB0038 Lime — **40** AB0040 Pale Grey — **41** AB0041 Ivory — **47** AB0047 Sea Blue — **69** AB0069 Yellow — **209** AB0209 Fluorescent Fire Orange

220 AB0220 Italian Red — **238** AB0238 Arrow Red — **239** AB0239 British Racing Green

Metallic **Colours** 14ml

11 AB0011 Silver — **12** AB0012 Copper — **16** AB0016 Gold — **52** AB0052 Baltic Blue — **53** AB0053 Gunmetal — **56** AB0056 Aluminium — **171** AB0171 Antique Bronze — **191** AB0191 Chrome Silver — **222** AB0222 Moonlight Blue

 Humbrol™ Rail Paints

The Humbrol range of acrylic railway colours was developed to suit the many variations found on the UK rail network during its almost 200-year history. These paints are also ideally suited for weathering, dry brushing and re-touching, taking your model railways hobby to a new level.

Matt **Colours** 14ml

RC401 AB2401 Dirty Black — **RC402** AB2402 Rust — **RC403** AB2403 Crimson Lake — **RC404** AB2404 Garter Blue — **RC405** AB2405 GWR/BR Green — **RC406** AB2406 Buffer Beam Red — **RC407** AB2407 BR Yellow — **RC408** AB2408 Apple Green — **RC409** AB2409 Malachite Green

RC410 AB2410 Maunsell Green — **RC411** AB2411 Diesel Blue — **RC412** AB2412 BR Coach Roof Grey — **RC413** AB2413 Engineers Grey — **RC414** AB2414 Executive Dark Grey

RC415 AB2415 Pullman Umber Brown — **RC416** AB2416 Pullman Cream — **RC417** AB2417 Coach Roof Off-White — **RC418** AB2418 EWS Red

RC419 AB2419 EWS Yellow — **RC420** AB2420 Orange Lining — **RC421** AB2421 Virgin Red

RC422 AB2422 Intercity Grey — **RC423** AB2423 Carmine — **RC424** AB2424 BR Cream

Humbrol™ Acrylic 14 ml e

Humbrol™ Acrylic Rail Colour 14 ml e

Turn your model kit into a masterpiece!

Weathering **Powders** 28ml

Humbrol Weathering Powders are a versatile means of adding realistic weathering effects to your models, figures and dioramas. They can be mixed to create different shades, enabling a full range of finishes including dust, mud, soot, rust and many more.

AV0001
Black

AV0002
White

AV0003
Sand

AV0004
Smoke

AV0005
Chrome
Oxide Green

AV0006
Iron Oxide

AV0007
Dark Earth

AV0008
Rust

Enamel **Washes** 28ml

Enhance your models with the Humbrol Enamel Washes range, designed for a wide range of uses they are easy to use and very durable.

Made in the UK

AV0201
Black

AV0202
White

AV0203
Dark Green

AV0204
Dark Grey

AV0205
Dark Brown

AV0206
Blue Grey

AV0207
Sand

AV0208
Dust

AV0209
Oil Stain

AV0210
Rust

Enamel **Effects** 28ml

Used to create realistic worn or chipping weathered effects.

Chipping Effect
AV1201 28ml bottle

Worn Effect
AV1202 28ml bottle

Turn your model kit into a masterpiece!

 Follow us!
www.twitter.com/humbrol

 **Like us!**
www.facebook.com/humbrol

 **Watch us!**
www.youtube.com/humbrol

118 Airfix | 2016 Yearbook

www.humbrol.com

Humbrol™ Spray Paints

Matt Colours 150ml

 1
AD6001
Grey Primer

 24
AD6024
Trainer Yellow

 27
AD6027
Sea Grey

 29
AD6029
Dark Earth

30
Dark Green

 33
AD6033
Black

34
AD6034
White

 63
AD6063
Sand

 64
AD6064
Light Grey

 67
XX
Tank Grey

 80
AD6080
Grass Green

86
AD6086
Light Olive

90
AD6090
Beige Green

93
AD6093
Desert Yellow

 106
AD6106
Ocean Grey

 155
AD6155
Olive Drab

 160
AD6160
German
Camouflage
Red Brown

237
AD6237
Desert Tan

 **Humbrol™ Acrylic Spray**
Craftwork and Model

- Peinture En Aerosol
- Sprayfarbe Spuitlak

Suitable for Plastic Kits,
Polycarbonate, Wood and Metal
For both Indoor and Outdoor use
150ml

Satin Colours 150ml

 85
AD6085
Black

 163
AD6163
Dark Green

 **164**
AD6164
Dark Sea Grey

 165
AD6165
Medium
Sea Grey

Gloss Colours 150ml

 3
AD6003
Brunswick Green

 14
AD6014
French Blue

 15
AD6015
Midnight Blue

 18
AD6018
Orange

 19
AD6019
Bright Red

 20
AD6020
Crimson

 21
AD6021
Black

22
AD6022
White

 38
AD6038
Lime

  68
AD6068
Purple

 69
AD6069
Yellow

 220
AD6220
Italian Red

 238
AD6238
Arrow red

 239
AD6239
British Racing
Green

Metallic Colours 150ml

 11
AD6011
Silver

  16
AD6016
Gold

  52
AD6052
Baltic Blue

 53
AD6053
Gunmetal

 54
AD6054
Brass

 55
AD6055
Bronze

 56
AD6056
Aluminium

191
AD6191
Chrome Silver

 201
AD6201
Black

All spray cans contain 150ml except where stated

A fast drying acrylic-based paint for use not only on plastic kits, but also on other substrates including, polycarbonate, wood, glass, ceramics, metal, card and many more, not to mention craft and DIY uses.

Fluorescent Colours 150ml

The New Humbrol Fluorescent spray range includes five bright colours, ideal for identification, safety, DIY and craft projects on a wide range of surface types. The spray also glows under UV light.

AD6202
Pink

AD6203
Green

AD6204
Yellow

AD6205
Orange

AD6210
Blue

Metalcote Colours 150ml

27002
AD6995
Polished
Aluminium

27003
AD6996
Polished Steel

Humbrol Metalcotes have been designed to give the appearance of polished metals. Once dry, polish with a soft cloth until you reach the desired look.

Acrylic Varnish 150ml

Suitable for applying over acrylic paint.

35
AD6035 Gloss
Varnish

49
AD6049 Matt
Varnish

135
AD6135 Satin
Varnish

Enamel Varnish 150ml

Suitable for applying over enamel paint.

35
AD6997 Gloss
Varnish

49
AD6998 Matt
Varnish

135
AD6999 Satin
Varnish

Textured Scenery Spray

The perfect accessory for creating textured effects on everyday items or for a diorama. Once dry the surface can be painted over to create a perfectly detailed street effect all the way to sand on your beach scene.

AD7551 150ml

Made in the UK

Multi-Effect **Sprays** 150ml
Create Two-Tones in one spray!

Ideal for a wide range of uses; plastic kits, slot cars, remote control subjects, along with decorative and craft projects.
Humbrol Multi-Effect Sprays must be applied on a black undercoat/surface.
To achieve optimum durability, we also recommend using Humbrol acrylic varnish.

AD6211
Gold

AD6212
Red

AD6213
Blue

AD6214
Green

AD6215
Violet

Glass **Etch** 150ml

Use Humbrol Glass Etch to transform mirrors, interior doors and windows. Used in conjunction with stencils, a wide range of designer effects can be created.

AD7700
Glass Etch
White

AD7701
Glass Etch
Pink

AD7702
Glass Etch
Blue

AD7703
Glass Etch
Green

Crystal **Clear** 150ml

An acrylic spray coating that goes on clear and stays clear. Clear protects wood, metal, plastic, ceramic, fabric and paper surfaces permanently.
Seals porous surfaces with a clear finish, which will not yellow with age.
Adds strength and water resistance – helps prevent tarnish and rust.

AD7550

Great for a whole range of activities; from painting your radio control car, or home décor to graphic design and general DIY projects.
Discover everything you need to get crafty with our spray range.

Turn your model kit into a masterpiece!

Made in the UK

Humbrol™
Work Station
a MUST for all modellers!

Please Note: Paints, brushes and other Humbrol products shown are not included.

The Humbrol Work Station has many features:

- Double depth sections for holding 9 x 14ml/12ml Humbrol Enamel or Acrylic pots, or 3ml Humbrol Acrylic pots.

- Double depth water cup holders, allow the modeller to place Humbrol 28ml products, such as; matt, satin & gloss cotes, Decalfix, Maskol, Clearfix, Thinners and Liquid Poly.

- Designed to fit the new Humbrol A4 Cutting mat within the working area

- Two mixing areas either side of the Cutting Mat.

- A4 Instruction sheet holder.

- Brush and tool holders.

- Easy to hold handles either side of the Work Station.

- Rubber feet, which allows the modeller to place on a flat surface.

AG9156

The Humbrol Work Station is manufactured from a tough and durable material that can't be melted by Humbrol Poly Cement.

Humbrol™
Tool Sets, Airbrush, Masking Tapes & Mats

Tool Sets

The kit modeller's tool set
Specifically designed for the Airfix and plastic kit modeller – sprue clippers, tweezers, needle file and knife; all designed for making the perfect model.
AG9150 – Small
AG9159 – Medium

A3 Cutting Mat
A4 Cutting Mat

The kit modeller's mat
The "Kit Modellers" Cutting Mat is a self-sealing cutting mat with graphics and scale markings to suit all categories of plastic modelling.
A3 AG9157
A4 AG9155

The full range of accessories is designed to meet every modeller's needs. Whether it is your first ever model build or your collection is in to the hundreds these products will help you get the most out of your build.

 Follow us!
www.twitter.com/humbrol

 Like us!
www.facebook.com/humbrol

 Watch us!
www.youtube.com/humbrol

All Purpose **Airbrush**

A great beginners airbrush to introduce the skill of airbrushing at a great value price. Use with cans of Humbrol Airbrush Propellant or a compressor. All purpose airbrush (blister)
AG5107

Airbrush **Powerpack**

Airbrush Powerpack
Airbrush powerpack 400ml
AV6941

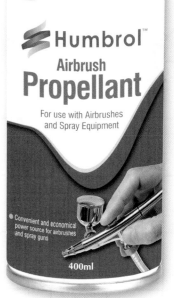

Humbrol™
coatings & thinners

Matt Cote

A solvent-based varnish that goes on clear and dries clear, overcoming the yellowing effect associated with traditional varnishes. The product dries to a smooth, low-sheen matt finish.

AC5601 28ml bottle

Satin Cote

A solvent-based varnish that goes on clear and dries clear, overcoming the yellowing effect associated with traditional varnishes. The product dries to a smooth, mid-sheen satin/eggshell finish.

AC5401 28ml bottle

Decalfix

A water based solution that softens decals and secures them in place by drawing the decal around and in any panel lines. Decals are permanent once dry.

AC6134 28ml bottle
AC7432 125ml bottle

Gloss Cote

A solvent-based varnish that goes on clear and dries clear, overcoming the yellowing effect associated with traditional varnishes. The product dries to a smooth, high-sheen gloss finish.

AC5501 28ml bottle

Maskol

A rubber solution that can be applied to surfaces to prevent them from being painted. When the paint has dried the Maskol can simply be peeled off.

AC5217 28ml bottle

Clear

These thin, water-based self-levelling varnishes are ideal for brush and airbrush. You have the option of three finishes, these are; Gloss, Matt or Satin with a higher level of any achieved by applying further thin coats.

AC7431 Gloss 125ml bottle
AC7434 Matt 125ml bottle
AC7435 Satin 125ml bottle

Acrylic Thinners

Humbrol Acrylic Thinners has been especially formulated to enhance the quality and usability of Humbrol Acrylic paint when brushing and airbrushing. The Thinners includes a retardant which reduces the drying rate and greatly improves the use of Acrylic paint when airbrushing. Can also be used to clean your brushes after use with Acrylic paint.

AC7433 125ml bottle

Enamel Thinners

Used to thin down Humbrol Enamel paints most commonly for airbrushing. Can also be used to thin down other solvent based products such as Enamel Washes, Modelcotes and Model Filler..

AC7501 28ml bottle
AC7430 125ml bottle

 Follow us! www.twitter.com/humbrol

 Like us! www.facebook.com/humbrol

 Watch us! www.youtube.com/humbrol

Humbrol™
adhesives and fillers

Poly Cement
24ml ℮
For Craftwork & Modelling

Poly Cement

A solvent-based cement suitable for plastic model kits only.

AE4021 12ml medium (tube)
AE4422 24ml large (tube)

Liquid Poly

A solvent-based cement suitable for plastic model kits only. The product is a lower viscosity version of Polycement to enable application by brush

AE2500 28ml bottle

Precision Poly Cement

A solvent-based cement suitable for plastic model kits only. Its viscosity is low to enable precision delivery of fine amounts of cement

AE5001 7ml precision poly dispenser
AE2615 14ml precision poly dispenser
AE2610 28ml precision poly dispenser

Balsa Cement
24ml ℮
For Craftwork & Modelling

Balsa Cement

A quick-drying transparent cement for balsa, soft woods and cork.
AE0603 24ml (tube)

Clearfix

A solvent-based polymer solution for use as an adhesive on clear plastic parts without the risk of the 'frosting' effect sometimes seen using traditional glues.
It can also be used for making small windows or translucent areas of 3mm or less.

AC5708 28ml bottle

Model Filler
31ml ℮
For Craftwork & Modelling

Model Filler

A fine grade model filler which can be sanded, filed and painted once dry.
AE3016 31ml (tube)

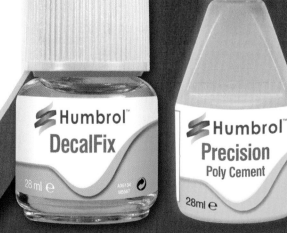

Coatings, Maskol, Decalfix, Clearfix, Model Filler and Thinners

Made in the UK

Turn your model kit into a masterpiece!

Humbrol™ Brushes

Coloro Brushes

The Coloro range of brushes are perfectly suited for all paint types, but are particularly good when used in conjunction with the new Humbrol Acrylic Paint. Made from man-made fibre

Size 00	– AG4030
Size 0	– AG4000
Size 1	– AG4001
Size 2	– AG4002
Size 4	– AG4004
Size 6	– AG4006
Size 8	– AG4008
Size 12	– AG4012

Coloro pack.
Size 00,1,4, 8 – AG4050

Evoco Brushes

Made from natural hair, Evoco brushes are the perfect "all-round" brush for many model and hobby uses, keeping their shape and quality long after their first use.

Size 000	– AG4131
Size 0	– AG4100
Size 2	– AG4102
Size 4	– AG4104
Size 6	– AG4106
Size 8	– AG4108
Size 10	– AG4110
Size 12	– AG4112

Evoco pack.
Size 0, 2, 4, 6 – AG4150

Palpo Brushes

The Palpo natural sable hair brushes are the ultimate modelling brush, keeping their points and shape to allow for accurate and detailed painting, particularly figure work.

Size 00000	– AG4233
Size 000	– AG4231
Size 0	– AG4200
Size 2	– AG4202
Size 4	– AG4204
Size 6	– AG4206

Palpo pack.
Size 000, 0, 2, 4 – AG4250

Detail Brushes

These ultra fine sable hair brushes are ideal for painting small detailed areas on your models/figures. The easy grip ergonomic handles make them a pleasure to use for short or long periods of time. Suitable for Enamel and Acrylic paints.

AG4301

Flat Brushes

Made from high quality soft synthetic hair, the Flat Brush pack is perfect for creating a smooth professional finish. Ideal for painting large surface areas, weathering, adding washes and helping to apply decals. Suitable for Enamel and Acrylic paints.

AG4302

Stipple Brushes

The Stipple Brushes have been designed with heavy dry brushing and weathering in mind. Made from a tough natural hair, which is perfect when adding those finishing touches when bringing your models to life. Suitable for Enamel and Acrylic paints, as well as Weathering Powder.

AG4303

Top tips on how to use Humbrol products are available at www.Humbrol.com. You can also see the products in action on the Official Humbrol YouTube Channel, www.youtube.com/Humbrol

 Follow us! www.twitter.com/humbrol

 Like us! www.facebook.com/humbrol

 Watch us! www.youtube.com/humbrol

Take your hobby to the next level

Visit us on our **You Tube** channel

HINTS

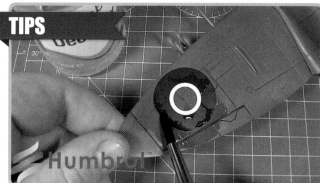

TIPS

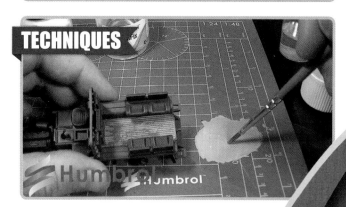

TECHNIQUES

www.youtube.com/Humbrol

▶ Constantly growing collection of videos

▶ Dedicated "How To" Playlist specifically highlighting how to use our products

▶ Great place for you to request videos that you would like Humbrol to do

▶ Collection of Weathering Techniques across multiple videos to help you become a pro

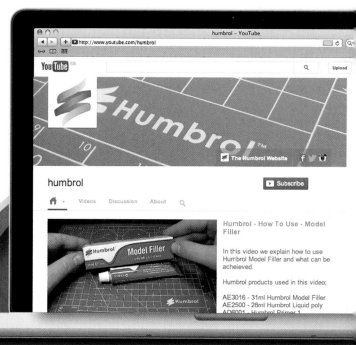

Humbrol™ on **You Tube**

Humbrol™ Product Chart

Paint Products	Usage	Substrate
Enamel Paint	A solvent-based, fast-dry paint developed for use on plastic model kits but which can also be used on other substrates (see right). Matt, Satin, Gloss, Metallic, Metalcote and Clear finishes are available.	A wide range of surfaces including most plastics, wood, glass, ceramics, metal, cardboard, sealed plaster, sealed hardboard and many more.
Acrylic Paint	A water-based, fast dry paint developed for use on plastic model kits but which can also be used on other substrates. Matt, Satin, Gloss, Metallic and Clear finishes are available.	A wide range of surfaces including most plastics, wood, glass, ceramics, metal, cardboard, sealed plaster, sealed hardboard and many more.
Acrylic Spray	A solvent-based, fast-dry paint developed for use on plastic model kits but which can also be used on other substrates (see right). Matt, Satin, Gloss, Metallic and Clear finishes are available.	A wide range of surfaces including most plastics, wood, glass, ceramics, metal, cardboard, sealed plaster, sealed hardboard and many more.
Textured Scenery Spray	Creates textured rough surface effect, to imitate rough surfaces such as tarmac and sand.	A wide range of surfaces including most plastics, wood, glass, ceramics, metal, cardboard, sealed plaster, sealed hardboard and many more.
Varnish Spray	Protects and creates a desired finish: Matt, Satin & Gloss.	Overcoat for the applicable paint type.
Fluorescent Spray	Creates instant visibility, idea for identification and safety as well as decorative and craft projects. Glows under UV light.	A wide range of surfaces including most plastics, wood, glass, ceramics, metal, cardboard, sealed plaster, sealed hardboard and many more. A white base coat must be applied first.
Multi-Effect Spray	Creates a Two-Tone / Flip paint effect.	A wide range of surfaces including most plastics, wood, glass, ceramics, metal, cardboard, sealed plaster, sealed hardboard and many more. A black base coat must be applied first.
Metal Cote Spray	Creates a polished look once dry and buffed.	A wide range of surfaces including most plastics, wood, glass, ceramics, metal, cardboard, sealed plaster, sealed hardboard and many more.
Glass Etch	Used to transform mirrors, interior doors and windows. Used in conjunction with stencils, a wide range of designer effects can be created.	Not suitable for areas prone to high condensation, steam, moisture or cold damp conditions.
Crystal Clear	Seals porous surfaces, finish will not yellow with age. Adds strength and water resistance – helps prevent tarnish and rust.	Wood, metal, plastic, ceramic, fabric and paper.
Weathering Powder	Used to create realistic weathered effects.	Weathering Powder can be applied to most substrates depending on the method. For full details, please visit the Humbrol website.
Enamel Wash	Used to create realistic weathered, oiled and grime effects on scale models.	Humbrol Enamel Washes can be applied to most substrates depending on the method. For full details, please visit the Humbrol website.
Enamel Effects	Used to create realistic worn or chipping weathered effects.	Enamel Effects can be applied to most substrates depending on the method. For full details, please visit the Humbrol website.

Glues	Usage	Substrate
Poly Cement	A solvent-based cement suitable for plastic model kits only.	Common plastics used to manufacture model kits including polystyrene and ABS. The product works by melting the plastic on application and 'welding' two glued pieces of plastic together to form a strong bond.
Model Filler	Fills hairline cracks and gaps between plastic parts. The product can be sanded when fully dry using a fine grade of sandpaper and painted.	Plastic model kits.
Balsa Cement	A quick-drying transparent cement for balsa, other soft woods and cork.	Balsa, other soft woods and cork.

Detail Application	Usage	Substrate
Clearfix	A solvent-based polymer solution for use as an adhesive on clear plastic parts without the risk of the 'frosting' effect sometimes seen using traditional glues and for making small windows or translucent areas of 3mm or less.	Common plastics used to manufacture model kits including polystyrene and ABS.
Decalfix	A water-based solution for softening decals and securing them into position.	Decals are usually applied onto painted surfaces. Care should be taken to avoid 'silvering' over matt paints.
Maskol	A rubber solution that can be applied to surfaces to prevent them being painted. When the paint has dried the Maskol can be simply peeled off.	Common plastics used to manufacture model kits including polystyrene and ABS and a wide variety of other applications including glass.
Enamel Thinner	Thinning down of solvent-based enamel paints, most commonly for airbrushing.	Enamel paint and other Humbrol solvent based products.
Acrylic Thinner	Thinning down of Humbrol Acrylic paints, most commonly for airbrushing.	Acrylic paint.

Finishing	Usage	Substrate
Mattcote/Satincote/ Glosscote	A solvent-based varnish that goes on clear and dries clear, overcoming the yellowing effect associated with traditional varnishes. The product dries to a smooth, low-sheen matt finish.	Common plastics used to manufacture model kits including polystyrene and ABS, as well as MDF. Matt cote is usually applied as the final coat to a fully painted and decaled model.
Clear	A water soluble, self-levelling medium in either gloss, matt or satin that can be used to prepare surfaces. Gloss varnish can be used to prepare surfaces for decals and to improve the appearance of clear parts.	Humbrol Enamel and Acrylic Paint.

 Follow us! www.twitter.com/humbrol   **Like us!** www.facebook.com/humbrol   **Watch us!** www.youtube.com/humbrol

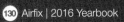